This Deperdussin monoplane becomes the first aeroplane to cover 200 kilometres (124 miles) in one hour, piloted by Maurice Prévost of France.

Sadi Lecointe of France goes faster than 300 km/h (188 m.p.h.) in a Nieuport.

Brown of America flies at over 400 km/h (259 m.p.h.) in an aeroplane designed by Curtiss.

Wendel of Germany flies at 755 km/h (469 m.p.h.) in a Messerschmitt Bf 109R. This was the last time the world air-speed record was held by a piston-engined aeroplane.

In a Gloster Meteor, Wilson of England sets the first record for a jet-propelled aircraft with a speed of 975 km/h (606 m.p.h).

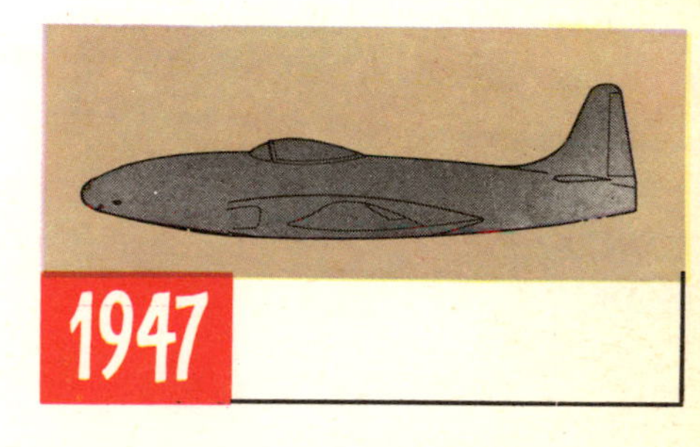

For the first time a speed of over 1,000 km/h (623 m.p.h.) is achieved - by Boyd of America in a Lockheed P-80R.

Irvin of America flies at 2,259 km/h (1,404 m.p.h.) in a Lockheed F-104 Starfighter.

In a supersonic interceptor, the McDonnell F-4 Phantom II, Robinson of America flies at 2,585 km/h (1,606 m.p.h.).

On 1st May Stephens and Andre of America set the current officially-recognised world speed record of 3,331.507 km/h (2070.102 m.p.h.) in a Lockheed YF-12A experimental fighter.

CONTENTS

Illustrated by Amedeo Gigli and Marcello Ralli

Captions: Paola Zammariotti

Aviation Consultant: Giorgio Bignozzi

The Story of FLYING

Hamlyn London New York Sydney Toronto

Translated by Bridget Galeotti
Published 1974 by
The Hamlyn Publishing Group Limited
London New York Sydney Toronto
Astronaut House, Feltham, Middlesex, England

ISBN 0 600 38151 X

Printed in Italy by OFSA - Casarile (Milano)

From the myth of Icarus to flying machines

Civilisation began when man first made simple tools and weapons in his struggle for survival. For thousands of years man has applied his intelligence to solving ever more complex problems. The discovery of the wheel gave him the means of moving rapidly over land. The conquest of water opened up the way to a series of important discoveries which permitted the most ancient civilisation we know of to navigate rivers, lakes and seas. But man has always looked to the conquest of the air as his crowning achievement. No one knows who was the first man to envy the birds of the air their freedom to fly as they wished through the boundless expanse of the sky: possibly he was the first man on earth. One thing is certain: that from the earliest of times, man not only envied the birds, but also thought to imitate their flight. Evidence of this comes from the ancient legends which tell of men who had the power to fly: a dream which made man almost equal to the gods. The Greek god Mercury, the messenger of the gods, was popularly portrayed with winged feet. Perhaps man's most poetic expression of the exhilaration and danger of flight

2

3

1 What mysterious power enabled birds to hover in the air, and to fly quickly from one place to another? This question tantalised primitive man, and led him to see flight as something magic or divine.

2 If the gods were much more powerful than men, then surely they could fly too. Thus primitive man started to imagine his gods as having wings. Illustrated here is the Egyptian goddess Isis.

3 One of the most famous legends of ancient Greece tells how Daedalus and Icarus tried to fly, in order to escape from the labyrinth. They made wings of feathers and wax, and flew through the sky, until the heat of the sun melted the wax and Icarus fell into the sea.

1

2

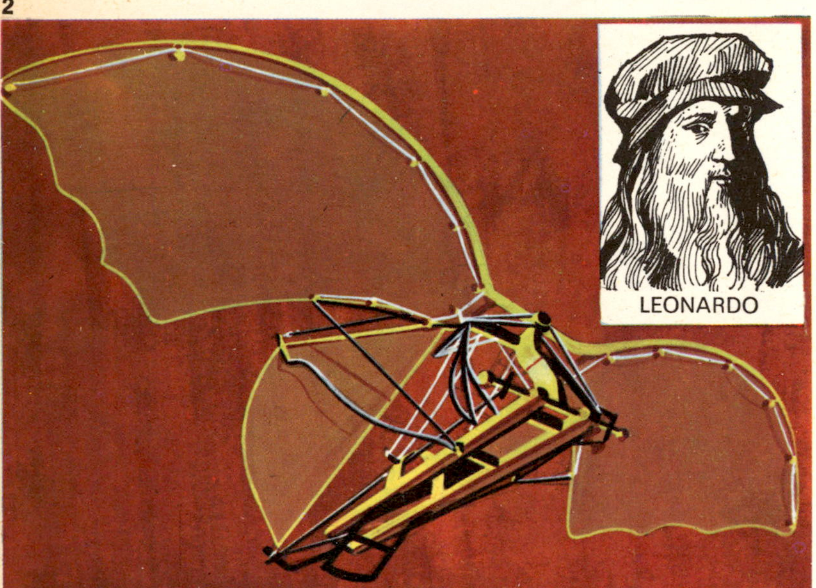

3

is found in the myth of Icarus. The unfortunate youth, who had dared to challenge the skies, has remained for thousands of years not only a fascinating and moving symbol of courage, but also an example to imitate if man was finally to become the undisputed master of his environment. In this age of space travel the attempts at flight made by brave men throughout the centuries, all of which failed miserably, may seem almost laughable, but these that great figure of the Italian Renaissance, which were useful to some extent, and as evidence of the ever-present desire to gain the freedom of the skies. It was, however, the genius of Leonardo da Vinci, that great figure of the Italian Renaissance, which produced the first amazing designs for "flying machines", which he planned in detail and sketched; Leonardo anticipated developments which have only

1 Illustrated here is an episode from the Bible, which tells of the flight of a man beloved of God. The prophet Elijah went up to heaven in a chariot of fire, drawn by two fiery horses which God had endowed with the power to fly.

2 Leonardo da Vinci must be considered a real pioneer of aeronautical design. In the sixteenth century he built a model of a helicopter, and produced drawings of various "ornithopters", which were intended to enable man to fly like the birds.

3 History tells of many attempts made by man to fly with artificial wings. At best, these attempts ended with a few broken bones, but only too often they proved fatal.

---

1 In the nineteenth century ideas on human flight became clearer. Air was thought of as a gas, capable of sustaining certain bodies, and the first gliders appeared. The Englishman Sir George Cayley was the great pioneer of aeronautical science and built the first successful man-carrying glider.

2 Drawing on the experience of flight enthusiasts all over Europe, Stringfellow built, in 1868, a powered model triplane which, however, he did not succeed in getting off the ground. It remained on show in London for several months.

3 The ornithopter designed by W. Miller in 1843 shows that the idea of imitating the flight technique of birds was not yet dead. Naturally not even this enormous mechanical bat could ever succeed in raising a man from the ground.

4 "It will fly over Philadelphia at 60 miles an hour!" With this sweeping statement W.J. Lewis presented in New York a curious design for a flying coach, with no fewer than six propellers. He never said how he was going to get these to rotate.

5 In 1847 the German Werner Siemens designed an aircraft which no longer depended solely on the whims of the wind. It was to be powered by the explosive force of gunpowder. The idea was the forerunner of the jet engine.

6 Russia, too, had her pioneers of flight. This big aeroplane, with steam-driven propellers, was built in 1884 by Alexander Mozhaiski. It hopped after gaining speed down a slope.

1

2

3

4

5

6

1

3

1 Otto Lilienthal of Germany is considered to be the most important pioneer of gliding. He made over two thousand flights with various designs. He was killed in an accident in one of his gliders in 1896.

2 In America Lilienthal had one of his greatest admirers in Octave Chanute, who only developed an interest in flying when he was over 60 years old. With the help of a friend who was an engineer, Chanute built a glider biplane in 1896, which proved reasonably stable in flight.

3 In the field of "lighter-than-air" craft, the Montgolfier brothers conducted the first successful experiment in 1783, when they made a balloon filled with hot air. In their honour hot-air balloons were called "montgolfiers".

4 The Montgolfiers were also the first to build a man-carrying balloon. On 21st November 1783, in the presence of the King of France, Pilâtre de Rozier and the Marquis d'Arlandes were the first men to fly freely in a montgolfier.

occurred in our time. The parachute, the aeroplane, and even the helicopter were all foreseen in the vivid imagination of this Italian genius. Naturally, Leonardo's inspiration derived from the birds. He studied the dynamics of their flight, and reached conclusions which, even today, are truly remarkable. However, little technical progress could be made on the basis of Leonardo's work, owing to a series of unfortunate circumstances, and his work was given careful study only towards the end of the nineteenth century. A great step forward in solving the problem of human flight was taken when it was realised that there were two possible ways of flying: as birds do — that is to say the flight of bodies heavier than air and as smoke or steam does — that is to say the tendency of gases which are lighter than air to rise.

1

2

3

4

Attempts to overcome the force of gravity, and so to overcome the power of the earth's pull with movement, failed miserably. Attention then turned to overcoming gravity with craft which were lighter than air. This came about thanks to the ingenuity of the Montgolfier brothers, who succeeded in getting the first man-carrying hot-air balloon off the ground. Thereafter these machines were known as "montgolfiers".

On what principle was this major breakthrough based? For us, two hundred years later, it seems obvious, but at the time it was certainly a fortunate discovery. A very light-weight paper bag was filled with hot air. The hot air, as it rose, carried the bag up with it. Man's first victory over air had occurred. The airships which flourished in the early

In competition with the Montgolfier brothers, the scientist, J.A.C. Charles designed and constructed balloons which used hydrogen, a very light gas, instead of rarefied hot air. His first man-carrying flight was made on 1st December 1783. 1

Balloons flew, but could only drift where the wind carried them. The next stage was to study how to navigate them. As a first step their shape was changed from spherical to oval. The first really functional airships were the work of Santos-Dumont. 2

Airships had engines and propellers fixed to a specially designed framework suspended from the gas-inflated envelope. In America the first airship was built in 1904 by Captain T.S. Baldwin, and named the "California Arrow". 3

The greatest builder of airships was the German, Ferdinand von Zeppelin. His craft, with constantly improved standards of comfort, were even used for regular passenger flights, and travelled the skies in all parts of the world. 4

twentieth century were basically very similar to the air-balloons of Montgolfier; but, like most balloons, they were filled with a gas such as hydrogen. They rose because this gas was lighter than air. Airships did, however, have serious defects. They were both difficult to manoeuvre and also extremely dangerous, as the gas contained in them was highly inflammable. In addition, the flight of "lighter-than-air" craft did not totally satisfy flying enthusiasts who still looked to the day when man would succeed in flying in a craft which was heavier than air. Over a century after man's first ascent in a montgolfier (15th October 1783) the age of mechanised flight was finally begun by the Wright brothers (17th December 1903). This great leap forward was only made possible by the development of the piston-engine, which enabled the aircraft to overcome the force of gravity. The first 59 seconds of flight, and the first 260 metres flown marked the true beginning of the era of air travel.

The 17th December 1903 marked the birth of the aeroplane as we know it. On that day, on the sands at Kitty Hawk, the Wright brothers succeeded in flying short distances in a powered aeroplane. The aircraft illustrated is a later version of the same design. 1

After their first successful experiment the Wright brothers continued to improve their aeroplanes, and to increase the distance they could fly. In 1908, however, Orville Wright's plane crashed. He survived the accident, but was seriously injured. 2

The Brasilian, Santos-Dumont, who had already distinguished himself in the construction of airships, also involved himself in aeroplane design, and produced the first powered aircraft to be flown before official observers in Europe. His biplane had its first successful flight in 1906. 3

The first European to become an aeroplane pilot was English-born Henry Farman, who had originally been a racing driver. In 1909 he began to build aeroplanes himself. Here we see him in flight on a Voisin biplane. 4

1

3

1 The first seaplane dates from March 1910. It was built by Henri Fabre of France. The great pioneer of flying off water was, however, Glenn Curtiss of America. When his seaplane was shown for the first time at San Diego in California, on 26th January 1911, it immediately aroused the interest of the US Navy.

2 On 19th July 1909 Hubert Latham attempted to fly across the English Channel, but his plane was forced down into the sea. Six days later his rival, Louis Blériot made a successful crossing, in only 37 minutes flight time.

3 All the time aeroplanes were being made safer, and brave pilots were embarking on new enterprises. In 1911 Calbraith P. Rodgers flew from coast to coast across. America, taking 49 days.

4 In the first heroic years of flight, aeroplanes had no cockpits, and pilots were exposed to wind and rain. For this reason they needed to muffle themselves up in heavy clothing, and this hindered their movements.

1

2

3

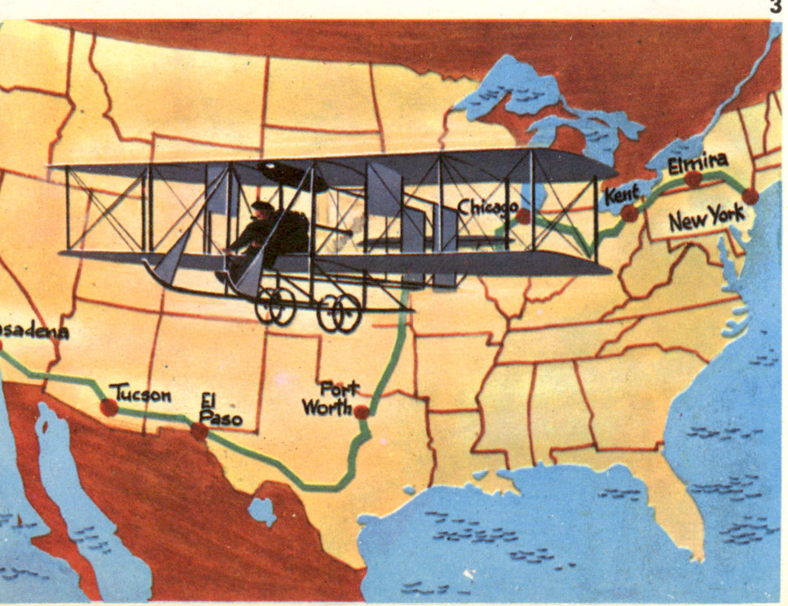

4

The huge Caproni 42 triplane, a bomber used by several countries during World War I.

THE RED BARON

Among the Knights of the Air, who engaged in battle in the skies over Europe during World War I, one of the most famous was Manfred Freiherr von Richthofen, nicknamed the Red Baron. Richthofen was the most famous German air ace, and in two years as a fighter pilot he shot down eighty enemy aircraft. In the first illustration he is shown in uniform. In the background is a Fokker Dr I — his favourite aeroplane, which he was piloting when he was shot down on 21st April 1918. In the second illustration we see Richthofen piloting an Albatros D II in action against a British reconnaissance aircraft. The third drawing reconstructs the scene when he was shot down.

Heroes of World War I

As always happens in the history of human progress, the ten years which followed the Wright brothers' first flight saw a succession of advances in the field of aeronautics which were little short of miraculous. On 29th September 1913 Maurice Prévost of France achieved an astounding record. With a French-made monoplane he reached the speed of 126.67 m.p.h. The first World War was imminent. Europe was about to undergo its first terrible bloodbath. Military needs gave a decisive push forward to the young aeronautical industry. Many nations saw the aeroplane as an effective weapon, which was not to be neglected. Italy had been the first to use aeroplanes in war, during the conquest of Libya in 1911. During the first World War, all the countries involved developed increasingly powerful and fast aircraft, which played an important military role, as fighters, as spotter planes and as the first bombers. After more than four years of war, the achievements of military aviation were astounding: the aircraft industry had really become established, 250 different types of aeroplane had been designed and 210,000 aircraft built. Every nation involved in the war had its famous pilots, among them the German, von Richthofen, nicknamed the Red Baron, the Englishman Edward Mannock and the American, Edward Rickenbacker. The heroism of these pilots undoubtedly contributed to the technical progress made in the field of civil aviation.

GEORGES GUYNEMER

Most famous ace of the French air force was Georges Guynemer who took part in 600 engagements, and shot down 54 enemy aircraft. At the beginning of the war he flew a Morane Bullet monoplane, and in this aeroplane he shot down his first enemy aircraft on 19th July 1915 (see second illustration). Later he preferred the stronger, faster SPAD, on one of which he mounted a heavy gun which fired through the propeller disc (third illustration).

GODWIN BRUMOWSKI

Austria had very few military aircraft. During the whole course of the war she built only 4,500 aircraft, as compared with 47,000 built by her ally, Germany. However, among her pilots was an ace of outstanding courage, Godwin Brumowski, who notched up 35-40 successes against the enemy, especially on the Italian front. Brumowski first flew a Hansa-Brandenburg D1 biplane, called the "Starstrutter", because of the unusual appearance of the crossed struts between the wings (see first and second illustrations). Later he and his squadron changed to the Albatros DIII, which proved faster, and which was armed with two synchronised machine-guns (third illustration). Brumowski survived the war, but was killed in an air accident in 1937.

EDWARD VERNON RICKENBACKER

Entering into the war late, the United States used almost exclusively aeroplanes built in Europe. Their most famous pilot was "Eddie" Rickenbacker, who gained his first victory, on 29th April 1918, while piloting a Nieuport 28 biplane, one of the fastest French fighter planes (see second illustration). Later he went on to fly the stronger SPAD XIII (first illustration), with which he took part in many successful engagements. In just one month (October 1918) he shot down 14 enemy aircraft. In the third illustration we see him in action against a 2-seater German Rumpler CIV.

EDWARD MANNOCK

The career of Edward Mannock, the British ace pilot, began with his shooting down a German observation balloon. The second illustration reconstructs the moment at which Mannock, on board his Nieuport "Bebe" is flying away from the first German Draken to be set on fire. Later on Mannock had at his disposal progressively faster and stronger aircraft, built by the British aviation industry in record time (55,000 aircraft of various types built in 4 years), and he was able to notch up no less than 73 victories over the enemy. His favourite aeroplane, during the latter months of the war, was the S.E.5a fighter which is shown in the third illustration flying away from a German biplane which has just been hit.

Fighter aircraft

From the point of view of military high command, spotter planes were possibly the most valuable. They could be used to gain vital information about the disposition of the enemy's forces, and artillery and troop movements. Bomber planes, if well used, could have considerable effect in harassing the enemy's rear, and in preparing the way for infantry advances. They did, however, have the great defect of being slow, and therefore presented an easy target for enemy fighters. But the aeroplanes which, more than any other during World War I aroused the enthusiasm of the young pilots were the fighters. In a sense these took the place of the chargers used in old-fashioned warfare, as witness the fact that many of the first fighter pilots came from the cavalry. To climb into a fighter plane was to have under you a craft which was manoeuvrable, easily controlled, swift, and armed with automatic weapons which were deadly at close range. Engagements between fighter planes were like duels between two knights of the air. Greater technical advances were also made in fighter planes, during the war years, than other types of aircraft. From the first fighters, which had to be controlled with only one hand, while the pilot used the other hand to fire the machine gun, fighters were developed which had their guns synchronised with the propeller, so that bullets could pass between the blades without hitting them. It is also true that more fighter planes were designed and built than any other type of aircraft. There were acts of true chivalry during World War I. War, with its inevitable slaughter, had not erased from the hearts of the young pilots their innate sense of humanity. On all the battle fronts there were many instances of compassion towards a beaten enemy, moments of truce in which, however briefly, the war was forgotten. In any case, one day the war would be over, and then there would be the excitement of meeting one's enemy of today in friendly competition.

FOKKER D VII
Germany
Wing span
8.93 m (29ft)
Length
7.21 m (23ft 7 ins)
Weight 880 kg
(1,940 lb)

HANRIOT HD I
Belgium
(French design)
Wing span
8.50 m (27ft 6 ins)
Length
7.21 m (23ft 5 ins)
Weight 575 kg
(1,268 lb)

SPAD S VII
France
Wing span
7.80 m (25ft 6 ins)
Length
6.10 m (19ft 10 ins)
Weight 755 kg
(1,664 lb)

NIEUPORT Ni 28
U.S.A.
(French design)
Wing span
8.35 m (27ft 5 ins)
Length
6.50 m (21ft 3 ins)
Weight 625 kg
(1,378 lb)

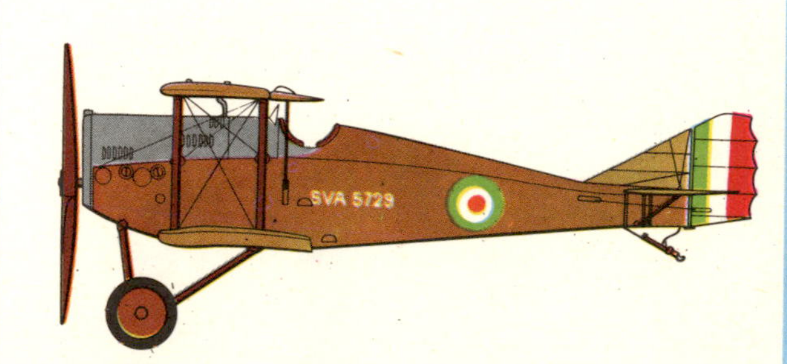

ANSALDO A.I. « BALILLA »
Italy
Wing span
7.68 m (25ft)
Length
6.50 m (21ft 1 ins)
Weight 885 kg
(1,951 lb)

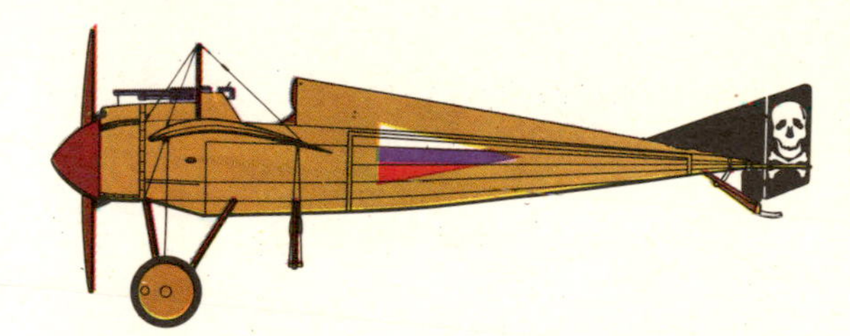

MORANE-SAULNIER TYPE N
Russia
(French design)
Wing span
7.20 m (23ft 5 ins)
Length
6.60 m (21ft 3 ins)
Weight 508 kg
(1,120 lb)

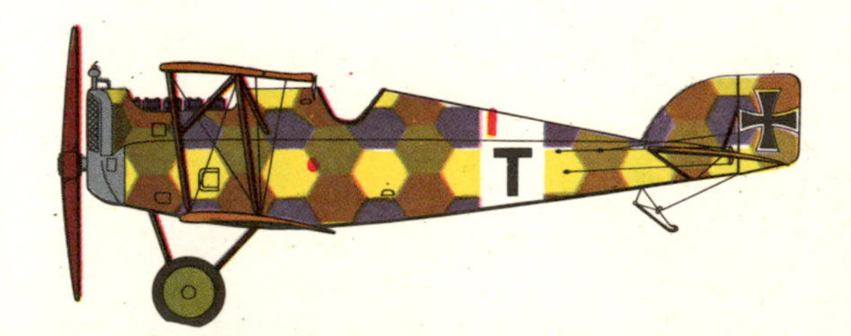

AVIATIK-BERG D. I.
Austria
Wing span
8 m (26ft 3 ins)
Length
6.80 m (22ft 2 ins)
Weight 882 kg
(1,945 lb)

BRISTOL F 2B
Great Britain
Wing span
11.96 m
(39ft 3 ins)
Length
7.975 m
(25ft 11 ins)
Weight 1,315 kg
(2,860 lb)

FAMOUS AIRCRAFT OF WORLD WAR I

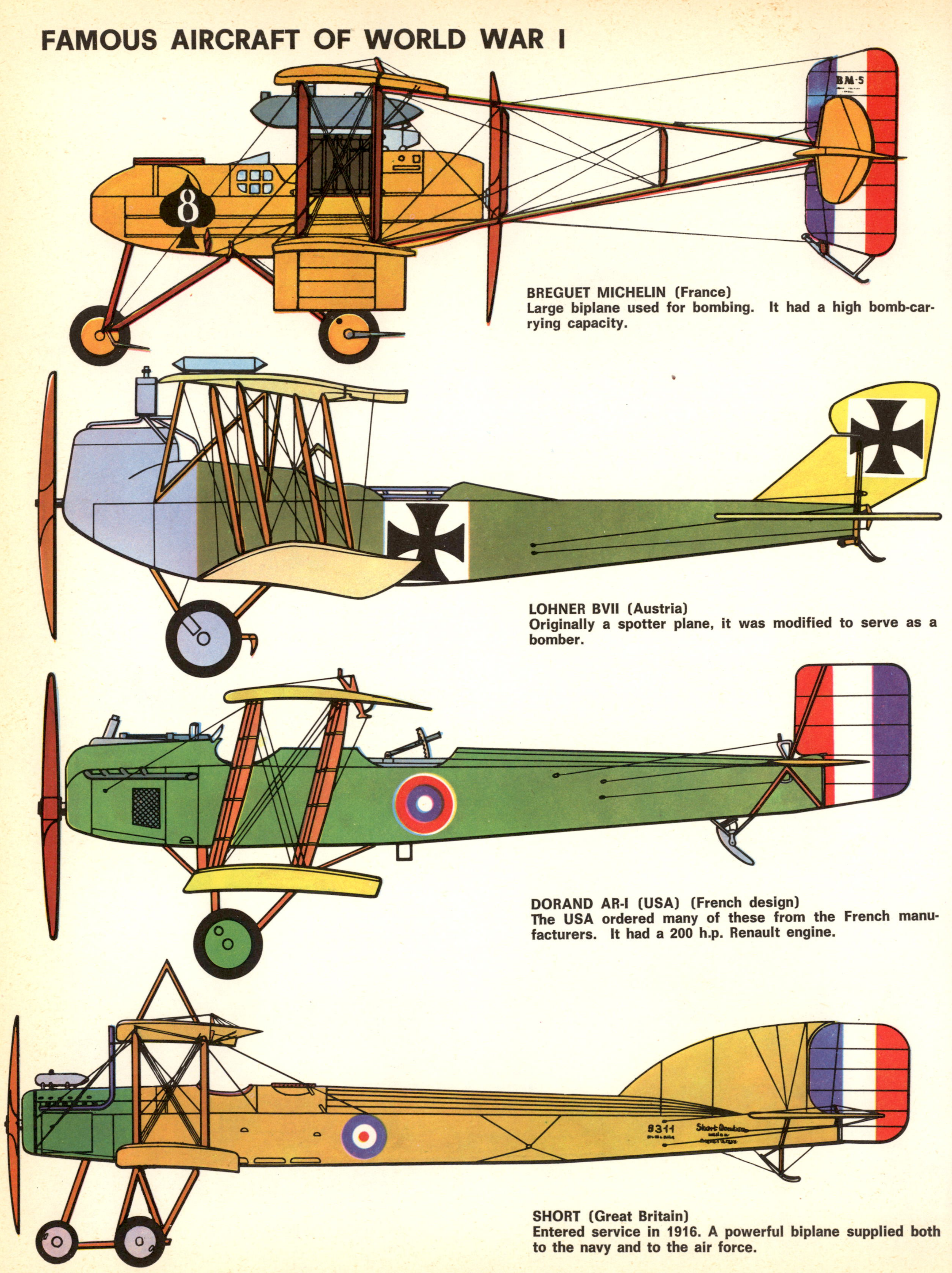

BREGUET MICHELIN (France)
Large biplane used for bombing. It had a high bomb-carrying capacity.

LOHNER BVII (Austria)
Originally a spotter plane, it was modified to serve as a bomber.

DORAND AR-I (USA) (French design)
The USA ordered many of these from the French manufacturers. It had a 200 h.p. Renault engine.

SHORT (Great Britain)
Entered service in 1916. A powerful biplane supplied both to the navy and to the air force.

FAMOUS AIRCRAFT OF WORLD WAR I

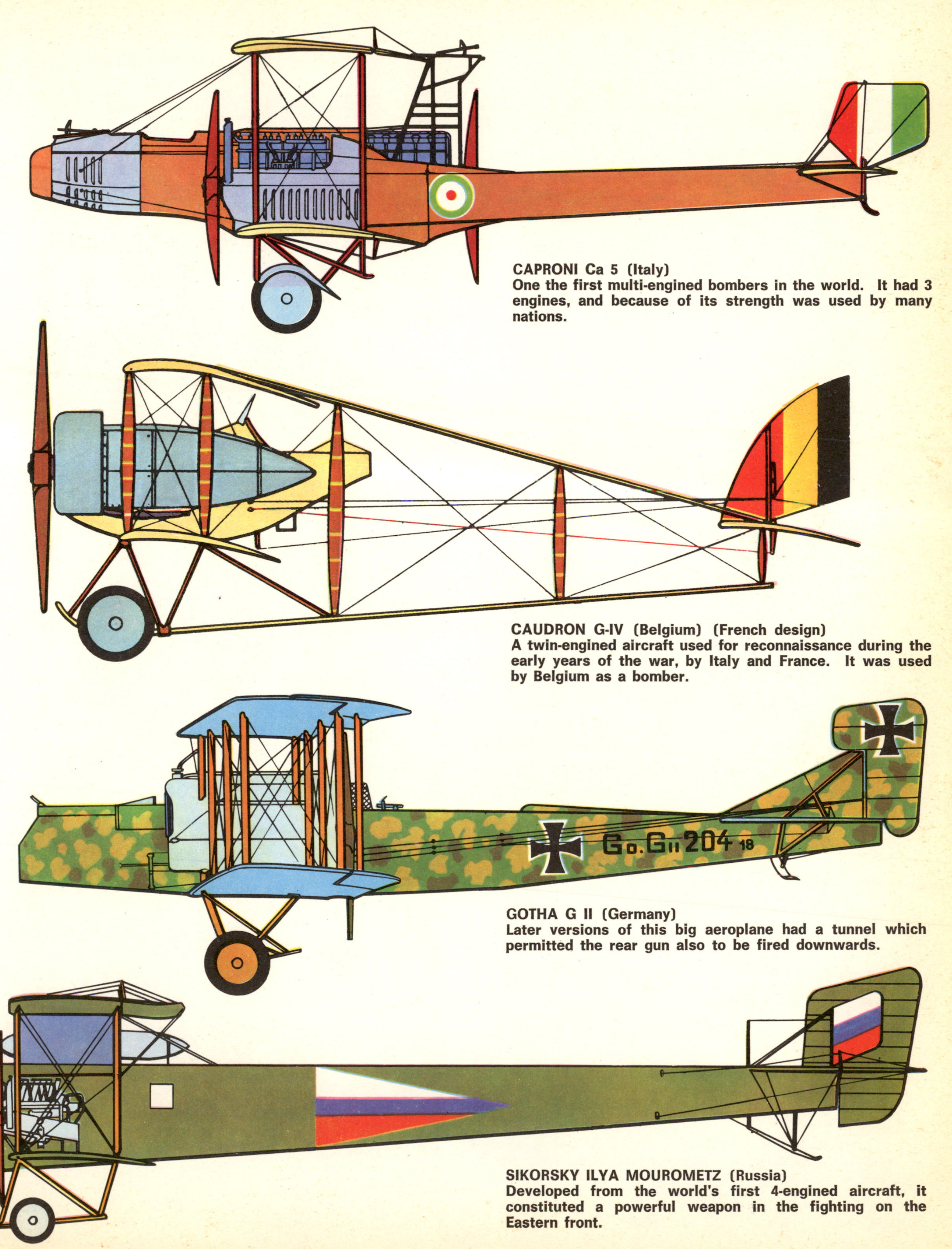

CAPRONI Ca 5 (Italy)
One the first multi-engined bombers in the world. It had 3 engines, and because of its strength was used by many nations.

CAUDRON G-IV (Belgium) (French design)
A twin-engined aircraft used for reconnaissance during the early years of the war, by Italy and France. It was used by Belgium as a bomber.

GOTHA G II (Germany)
Later versions of this big aeroplane had a tunnel which permitted the rear gun also to be fired downwards.

SIKORSKY ILYA MOUROMETZ (Russia)
Developed from the world's first 4-engined aircraft, it constituted a powerful weapon in the fighting on the Eastern front.

Transport takes to the air

At last the war was over. Some people thought aeroplanes were no longer of any use. What was the point, they argued, of using a means of transport which was so expensive, and so unsafe? But by now it was too late to halt the progress of aviation. The war had demonstrated how, in a short time, it was possible to overcome technical difficulties which had been thought insurmountable. Before the war, the first experiments with airmail had been conducted in India, Britain and other countries. In 1914 the first passenger flights had been organised in Florida — with one passenger to each aeroplane. Post-war aviation continued to develop in this direction, with ever increasing momentum. The future of the industry lay with civil aviation. The first commercial airline was organised in Germany, adapting military aircraft for passenger and freight transport. Soon England and France followed this example. One type of aircraft which proved eventually particularly suitable for commercial aviation was the flying-boat. First developed in 1911, and progressively improved during the war, it was notable for the fact that it could land on water. In ten years civil aviation made enormous advances, and the aeroplane decisively ousted the airship which, by now, was coming to the end of its era, with the famous Zeppelins. From the military point of view, the more widespread acceptance of the parachute was of great importance, giving the pilot the possibility of escape in case of accident. By the 1930's people had come to accept aeroplanes as a normal means of transport.

1 The first World War had given an enormous impetus to the aeronautical industry: in 60 months 210,000 aircraft had been built. After the war thought was given to using the aircraft for transporting mail. In the picture, the "Jenny", one of the first US aeroplanes used for transporting mail.

2 Many aeroplanes which had been used in the war were later modified to take passengers. Civil aviation was born in 1919 and developed rapidly. One of the most comfortable aeroplanes was this Rumpler C IV, with its roomy cabin.

3 A particularly important role in the development of civil aviation was played by Germany, which had been forbidden by the terms of the armistice to build any more military aircraft. The German factories had already the capacity to build up to 1,000 aeroplanes a month. Illustrated here is a Junkers F-13 monoplane.

1

2

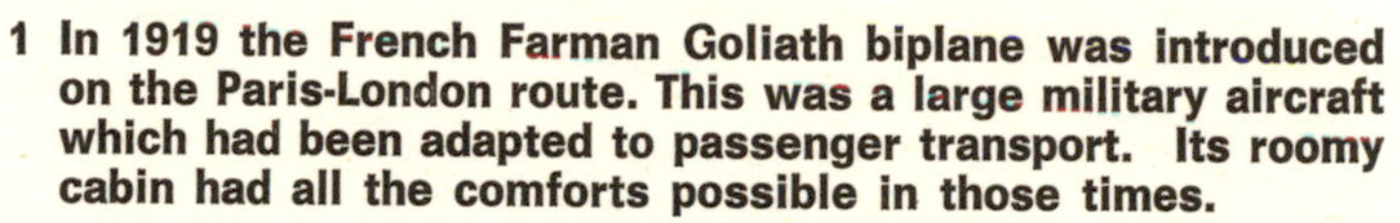

1 In 1919 the French Farman Goliath biplane was introduced on the Paris-London route. This was a large military aircraft which had been adapted to passenger transport. Its roomy cabin had all the comforts possible in those times.

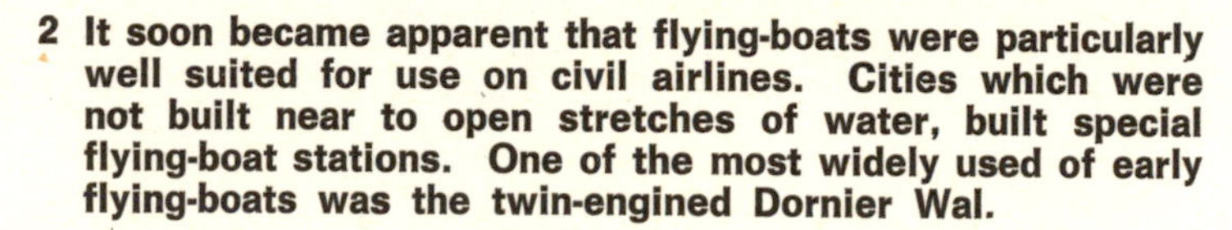

2 It soon became apparent that flying-boats were particularly well suited for use on civil airlines. Cities which were not built near to open stretches of water, built special flying-boat stations. One of the most widely used of early flying-boats was the twin-engined Dornier Wal.

3

4

3 The Fokker F. VII was an early aeroplane designed and built specifically for passenger transport. Its first scheduled flight between London and Holland was inaugurated in June 1924. It was famous for its luxurious 8 seater cabin.

4 Freight transport by air was also developing all the time, and the aviation industry developed specially designed aircraft, with very wide fuselages, like this Junkers G-31 which could even take a motor car, as well as other cargo.

1

3

1 The years passed, and flying became accessible to everyone. The year 1934 saw the introduction of the first of a long line of larger aircraft — the Douglas DC-2. This remained in service for many years, proving itself to be safer and more comfortable than most earlier types.

2 The year 1936 brought the large high-speed Short "C" class flying-boats, in which it was possible to cross even the Atlantic in safety. One model of this aeroplane was equipped to launch a smaller seaplane in flight.

3 In America Sikorsky, Martin and Boeing built large flying-boats for civil use called "Clippers". These were heavy 4-engined aircraft, and the Boeings were used on the regular transatlantic crossings which began in 1939.

4 Airships tried to compete with the aeroplane, offering increased comfort and concentrating on a high standard of passenger accommodation. In 1929 the beautiful "Graf Zeppelin" entered service, and made a round-the-world trip.

5 The airships' prestige suffered a heavy blow in 1928 when Nobile's "Italia" crashed, after flying over the North Pole. The end of their era as passenger-carriers came in 1937 when the "Hindenburg" burst into flames while landing at Lakehurst.

The birth of the parachute

1

2

3

4

1 The first serious design for a parachute dates back to Leonardo da Vinci who sketched the design and workings of one in his "Codice Atlantico". In 1595 Fausto Veranzio designed this parachute, based on Leonardo's work. It was never tested.

2 The first experiments with parachutes only became possible when man had learnt how to raise himself from the ground with balloons. In 1797 Garnerin of France was carried up in the air with a parachute suspended from a montgolfier. He then released the balloon and made a safe landing with the parachute.

3 Parachutes proved invaluable during the first World War, but were used mainly by crews of tethered observation balloons, to escape when their highly inflammable craft were hit. An early light back-packed parachute was built in 1924 by Prospero Freri. It was made of 24 sections of fabric.

4 Once proven safe, the parachute was adopted by all air forces and perfected in its detail. Between 1935 and 1939 the first parachute corps were established, which were to be used in war in tactical operations.

Gliders

Man had, for centuries, aspired to wheel and soar through the sky like a bird. With the advent of the aeroplane, had this ambition been realised? For some, the answer was "no". These were the "purists" of flight, men dedicated to the idea of flying without any dependence on engines or propellers, but purely by the power of man's own abilities. These fervent romantics had not ceased their daring attempts at free flight ever since the first attempt to fly with wings made of feathers. Such attempts led, during the closing years of the last century, to the development of gliders, pioneered by the German, Otto Lilienthal. With the construction of the glider, the dream of natural flight seemed to have been achieved, but it was only a partial victory. The glider is, in fact, a type of craft which gives full expression to the pilot's expertise. It has, however, limited possibilities. Being built very like a normal aeroplane, it has to be catapulted off the ground or towed into the air by an engine-powered aircraft. Thereafter, really able pilots can keep it airborne for hours, by using the aircurrents wisely and by expert handling of the delicate controls. Like great gulls, gliders swoop, bank, climb and float through the air. This is, indeed, flying for the purist.

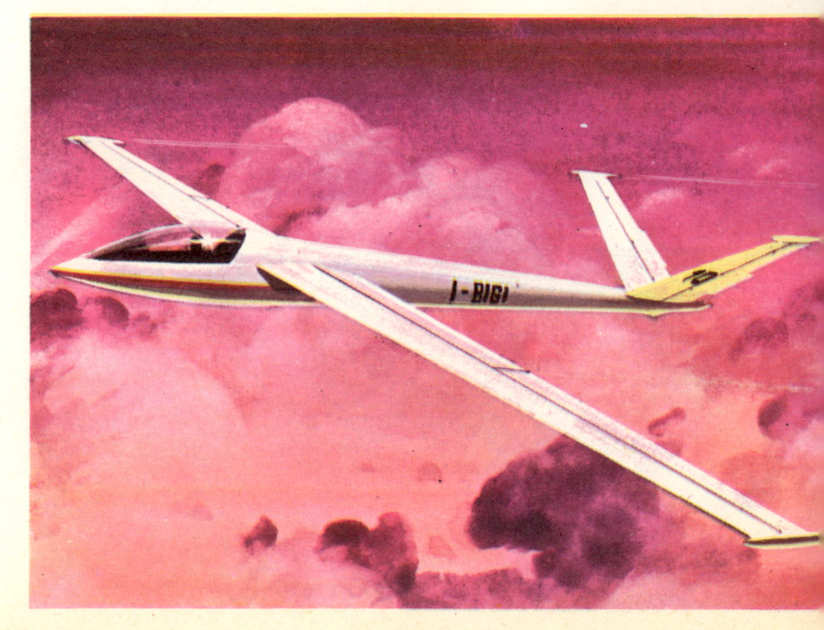

1 Enthusiasm for engine-driven aeroplanes had relegated to second place the old gliders, which had contributed so much to man's final conquest of the air. But after 1920 there was a resurgence of interest in flying without an engine. Here we see the Zogling.

2 It was above all Germany, forced to abandon military production, which developed a really serious glider industry, fostering several important international competitions. One of the most elegant of the German gliders was this Mínimoa.

3 Today gliding is an exciting sport which attracts thousands of young people. The gliders which take part in competitions have been developed to near perfection, with fine aerodynamic lines.

Route proving and competitive flying

The military or commercial uses to which aeroplanes were inevitably put did not quench the spirit of sportsmanship which was so alive in all fliers. Rivalry was transferred from the battlefield to the calmer, though none the less exciting air routes, on which not only the technical capabilities of the aircraft could be demonstrated, but also the skill and daring of the pilots. The years between the first and second World Wars saw a virtually uninter-

1 

2 

1 **As a result of the great efforts made by aircraft designers and manufacturers in the first World War, aircraft had reached the stage of technical capability where they could even attempt to cross the Atlantic. First across, via the Azores, was this NC-4 flying-boat of the US Navy in 1919.**

2 **Pilots, returning from the war, were not prepared to resign themselves to inactivity. New records were being established all the time. In 1923 Lieutenants Macready and Kelly flew this Fokker T-2 from coast to coast across America, taking almost 27 hours.**

3 **Pilots were also attracted by the challenge of the polar routes. On 9th May 1926, Richard E. Byrd and Floyd Bennett set off from Spitsbergen in this 3-engined Fokker, and despite contrary winds they reached the North Pole in 9 hours flying time.**

4 **In 1928 the airship "Italia" crashed. Many aircraft flew over the frozen wastes of the North Pole in search of survivors. The polar route was now open. In 1937 this Russian aeroplane made the first record-breaking flight on a polar route.**

3 

4 

Shown here are the routes of some of the most important non-stop long-distance flights completed between 1919 and 1949.

A - In 1919 two Englishmen, Alcock and Brown made the first non-stop transatlantic crossing, from Newfoundland to Ireland, in a twin-engined Vimy like this standard RAF bomber.

B - In 1928 Ferrarin and Del Prete of Italy established a new distance record, flying from Rome to Tourus (Brazil) in an S. 64.

C - In 1929 Costes and Bellonte of France flew from Paris to Chichihar in China, in a Breguet XIX.

D - In 1933 Codos and Rossi flew from New York to Rayak in Syria, on board a Blériot 110.

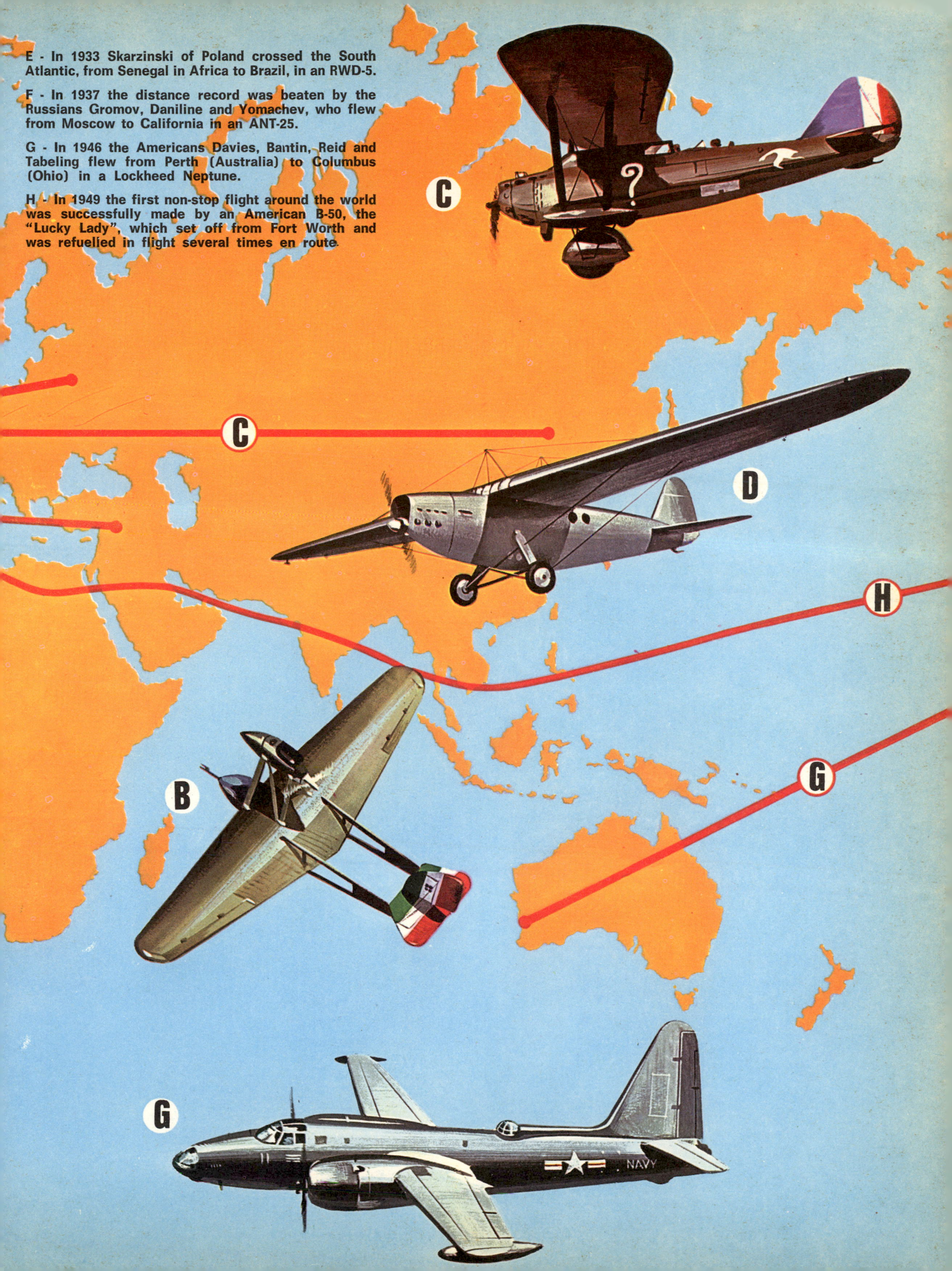
E - In 1933 Skarzinski of Poland crossed the South Atlantic, from Senegal in Africa to Brazil, in an RWD-5.
F - In 1937 the distance record was beaten by the Russians Gromov, Daniline and Yomachev, who flew from Moscow to California in an ANT-25.
G - In 1946 the Americans Davies, Bantin, Reid and Tabeling flew from Perth (Australia) to Columbus (Ohio) in a Lockheed Neptune.
H - In 1949 the first non-stop flight around the world was successfully made by an American B-50, the "Lucky Lady", which set off from Fort Worth and was refuelled in flight several times en route.
C
C
D
H
B
G
G
NAVY

1

3

1 **On 20th May 1927 Lindbergh set off from New York aboard his aeroplane the "Spirit of St. Louis", to attempt the solo crossing of the Atlantic. He was without a radio or sophisticated navigational instruments. Just 33 hours 30 minutes later he landed at Le Bourget airport in Paris.**

2 **The sturdiness and large fuel-carrying capacity of flying-boats made them particularly suitable for long-range flying. One of the most impressive flights was made in 1933 when 24 Italian flying-boats, under the command of Italo Balbo, made the return crossing between Italy and the USA.**

3 **In 1933 Wiley Post made a solo flight around the world in his Lockheed Vega. It took him 7 days 18 hours. This was a record-breaking performance. Two years earlier Post, accompanied by H. Gatty, had taken 8 days 16 hours for the same trip.**

4 **International competitions contributed a great deal to improvements in aircraft and to the establishing of new records. The American air race organised in 1920 by the Pulitzer brothers was won by this Verville-Packard, at a speed of 155 m.p.h.**

rupted succession of breath-taking exploits: from the Atlantic crossing by the "flying fool" Lindbergh, to Wiley Post's round-the-world flight and the transatlantic crossing by Italian flying-boats, and still-remembered racing and record-breaking flights. Sporting competition was looked on with great favour by the aircraft manufacturers, who viewed every success or record-breaking flight as a highly effective way of publicising their aeroplanes, at a time when commercial aviation was still in its infancy. Lindbergh's achievement, in particular, captured the imagination of the public throughout the whole world. He was the first man ever to attempt the solo crossing of the Atlantic. Everyone thought he was mad to try such a thing. It was the 20th May 1927. Not even the conquest of the moon, which 42 years later marked the end of one era and

1

2

3

4

1 One of the fastest aircraft of the 1930's was the Gee Bee, designed by Bob Hall. In 1932 one of these aeroplanes won the Thompson trophy, flying at 252 m.p.h. Gee Bees were capable of high speeds, but a number of pilots were killed in them.

2 Despite difficult flying conditions Lualdi and Bonzi of Italy succeeded in crossing the Atlantic in this light aircraft, named Grifo. The aeroplane was nicknamed "The Children's Angel" because the trip was made to collect funds for crippled children.

3 In 1934 Francesco Agello, flying a Macchi-Castoldi 72 seaplane, won the world speed record for Italy, with an average speed of 440.69 m.p.h. This seaplane record has never yet been broken. Agello was nicknamed the "Lightning Man".

4 May 1961. It is 34 years since Lindbergh's "Spirit of St. Louis" made its historic flight. Following the identical route, William Payne repeated the flight in a B-58. He flew from New York to Paris in 3 hours 19 minutes 44 seconds, but refuelled in the air three times during the crossing.

the beginning of another, aroused such deep emotion in the hearts of people the world over, as did Lindbergh's historic flight. But only three years later, the Atlantic was the scene of yet another spectacular crossing, this time by twelve Italian Savoia-Marchetti flying-boats. This successful attempt helped to point the way, eventually, to air travel between the Old and the New World. Crossing the Atlantic was no longer a dangerous adventure, but would soon become a part of everyday life. Mention should be made of Arturo Ferrarin, a brilliant pilot whose achievements, however, are too often overlooked. In 1920 — seven years before Lindbergh's famous crossing — and again in 1928, he made two exceptional flights, the first from Rome to Tokyo, and the second from Italy to Brazil. With the approach of the second World War competitive flying started to decline.

Formations of B-24 and B-17 bombers, escorted by long-range fighters.

WALTER NOWOTNY

In less than twenty years the fragile craft of World War I had been transformed into highly developed and fearsome aeroplanes. These were used in the second World War as instruments of death. Terrible battles took place in the air. The youngest ace pilot of the German Luftwaffe was Walter Nowotny who was already in charge of a flight of Me 109 fighters when he was only 22 years old. In the course of the war he achieved 258 victories over the enemy. He himself always emerged miraculously unhurt from the barrage of fire into which he flew so fearlessly. In the second illustration we see him going into the attack against some American B-25 Mitchell bombers. On the 15th March 1945 he was shot dead by an RAF Tempest, as he was coming in to land (third illustration).

Ace pilots of World War II

With the second World War, air power really came into its own as a battle-winning and war-winning service, particularly when it was not tied to the day-to-day requirements of armies on the ground. The RAF had been a fully independent service since 1918. Twenty years of exceptional advances in the field of aeronautics separated the military planes of World War I — which were largely biplanes — from the new ultra-fast and powerful monoplanes used in the second World War as bombers, fighters and reconnaissance aircraft. Structural modifications had been necessitated by the higher speeds which resulted from the use of more powerful engines. By the beginning of the war, aeroplanes were over three times faster than those used in 1914. But what made aircraft so formidable an arm in the second World War was, above all, the greatly increased size of bombers, the manoeuvrability of fighters, and the powerful weapons with which all types of aircraft were equipped. A tragic testing-ground for weapons that would be used later, in the second World War, was provided by the wars in Ethiopia and Spain, in which new bombing techniques, such as saturation bombing and dive bombing were tried and found successful, and bombs of much increased destructive power were dropped — fragmentation and incendiary bombs. Unfortunately the deadly effects of these aircraft did not arouse sufficient alarm in world-wide public opinion, and so, in 1939, war broke out — the war whose final outcome was to be decided by the new weapon of air power. The major problem facing the designers of military aircraft was to strike the right balance between their aircraft's speed, weight of weapons and armour plating, and range. The heavier and faster an aeroplane, the shorter its range often proved. Reduction in weight would give increased speed, but might lessen the aeroplane's military effectiveness, both in attack and in defence. A fighter might have a range of around 400-450 miles, and this was often not enough to escort bombers on long-distance raids. That was why the large

SABURO SAKAI

A pilot's bravery is not demonstrated only by the damage he inflicts on the enemy, but also by his ability to defend himself and to escape when attacked by superior forces. The Japanese ace, Saburo Sakai showed this ability on 24th June 1943. He had only just started to fly again, after an accident in which he had lost an eye, when he found himself surrounded by 15 Hellcats, which opened fire on him (second illustration). By skilful manoeuvring, Sakai managed to get back to base unharmed. Not even one enemy shot had hit his aeroplane. A few days before the end of the war, Sakai, together with Jiro Kawaci, firing at close range, succeeded in shooting down a huge American Superfortress (third illustration).

IVAN KOZHEDUB

Ivan Nikitievitch Kozhedub was nearly always fated to be fighting against overwhelmingly superior enemy forces, but he went out of his way to look for such engagements. This Russian ace pilot gained his first victory on 5th July 1943. He was piloting an La-5 when he intercepted a formation of German Junkers 87's. He swooped down on them, and with daredevil skill managed to force one down (second illustration). His greatest feat of bravery occurred on 17th April 1945, in the skies over Berlin. Together with Titorenko he went into the attack against a heavily armed formation of German fighter-bombers. He shot down two, and put the rest to flight (third illustration). Kozhedub was three times awarded the highest military decoration of the Soviet Union.

P. H. CLOSTERMANN

When France was overrun by the German army, this did not stop the French ace, P.H. Clostermann from gallant action against the enemy as a fighter pilot. Having escaped to England, Clostermann joined the RAF and flew a Spitfire at first, and later a Tempest. The second illustration recalls one of his most daring exploits. On 26th March 1945, on an armed reconnaissance flight, his squadron destroyed seven trains, in the Dummer region, and damaged many others, with the loss of only one aircraft. The French ace was seriously injured on 28th March 1945, as he made a crash landing in his badly damaged Tempest (third illustration).

271

JAMES EDGAR JOHNSON

To be awarded five medals for bravery is an outstanding achievement, but Group Captain James Edgar Johnson was worthy of even greater recognition, for his memorable exploits during the war. With his 38 victories Johnson gained the title of the RAF's greatest ace. He flew a Supermarine Spitfire, and in this fighter he chased German aircraft, following relentlessly in their wake until his repeated attacks sent them crashing down. In the second illustration we see a German Me 109E hit by his Spitfire in 1941. His most memorable exploits took place during 1942 against German Focke-Wulf 190 aircraft, which were considered fearsome opponents (see third illustration).

DOUGLAS R. S. BADER

Group Captain Douglas Bader of the RAF had lost both his legs, and was fitted with artificial limbs. Despite such a severe disability, he commanded a group of Spitfires, and took part in many stirring assignments, shooting down 22 enemy aircraft. On 30th April 1941, Bader's group, flying Hurricanes, went into action against a large formation of German Do 215s. After fierce fighting they shot down twelve of the enemy aircraft, without any loss to themselves (second illustration). Towards the end of the war his aeroplane crashed into an Me 109 (third illustration), and Bader was taken prisoner. The Germans admired his courage so much that they allowed a British fighter to parachute down some new artificial limbs for him, while he was in the prison camp.

bombers were well equipped to defend themselves against attack, some being armed with as many as eight cannons and four machine-guns. Their lack of speed was sometimes their great weakness. In the course of the war, however, aeroplanes were developed which combined the characteristics of reconnaissance aircraft or bombers with those of fighters. Reconnaissance was even more important in World War II than it had been in the first World War. This was because of the different type of warfare, which was far less static, and made up of sudden unexpected attacks, and of massive movements of troops and armoured columns. One instrument which proved decisive to the outcome of the war, and which gave the British a clear advantage in the field of long-range detection of aircraft, was radar. By its use, the position of an enemy aircraft could be plotted accurately and well in advance of its arrival. While aircraft had mastery of the skies, they still needed safe ground bases, as near as possible to the target, given the problems of range which have already been mentioned. However, it was not always easy to have bases which were big enough and well defended, in the right place. It was to solve this problem that aircraft carriers were built in increasing numbers during the second World War. These were real floating airports with a runway which was large enough for military aeroplanes to take off and land — fighters, reconnaissance aircraft, light bombers and torpedo bombers. Unlike the first World War, the final outcome of the second World War was largely decided by air power. Mankind had to pay a terrible price for peace to be restored to the world. Thousands upon thousands

of bombers dropped tons of bombs upon the towns, in an attempt not only to destroy military installations, but also to break the morale of the civilian population.

The Battle of Britain represents the finest hour for the pilots of the second World War.

In 1940 the Luftwaffe launched an all-out attack, seeking to bring Britain to her knees, with terrible bombing raids.

The best pilots of both countries fought in the skies over England. For a long time the result hung in the balance, while many men of both the British and German air forces fell, one after the other, as in the tournaments of old.

"Never in the field of human conflict was so much owed by so many to so few," said Churchill.

The "few" were the pilots of the RAF who, in their legendary Hurricanes and Spitfires, succeeded finally in overcoming the enemy forces, and Britain was saved.

1

2

3

Famous air battles

1 On Ist September 1939 German bombs rained down on the stations and airports of Poland, destroying many of her aircraft on the ground. It was the beginning of the second World War. In the dive-bombing raid illustrated the German Stukas proved deadly.

2 Huge air-sea battles took place in the Mediterranean in 1942. Here we see in action an Italian S. M.79 bomber, also used as a torpedo bomber. The British called these planes "damned hunchbacks" because of the gun-turret protruding from the cockpit.

3 On the Eeastern front in 1942, the Russian Stormoviks harassed the German land forces. These aeroplanes were heavily armoured and well equipped with weapons, and attacked and destroyed enemy tanks with their deadly rocket missiles.

---

1 The attack on the American naval base at Pearl Harbor, in the Pacific, signalled the beginning of hostilities with Japan, in 1941. Almost all the ships anchored there were put out of action. The only one to escape was an aircraft carrier which had left a few hours before on a naval exercise.

2 The Battle of the Pacific refers to the many engagements which took place in 1944 and 1945, between the Japanese and the Americans. Although they had no chance of winning, the Japanese did all they could to resist the crushing superiority of the American forces. This was the period of the incredible suicide attacks by the Kamikaze pilots.

3 The Americans' first effective reaction, after the disaster of Pearl Harbor, took place on 18th April 1942. On that day a group of B-25 bombers under the command of General Doolittle, took off from an aircraft carrier, and attacked Tokyo, the capital of Japan.

4 Towards the end of the war Germany built a new type of aircraft, which was intended to rout the American bomber formations. This was a high-speed rocket fighter, the Me 163 Komet. However, few of these were ever completed by the factories, which were by then virtually in ruins.

5 Gliders were also widely used during the war. Here we see the large transport gliders used by the Allies for the Normandy landing. By using these it was possible to transport into enemy territory a large number of men and vehicles, with very few losses.

6 The last act of the second World War was played out against the background of the huge sinister mushroom cloud of the atomic bomb. The first of these terrible bombs was dropped on Hiroshima, by an American B-29 on 6th August 1945. The second destroyed Nagasaki.

1

2

3

4

5

6

FAMOUS FIGHTERS OF WORLD WAR II

MESSERSCHMITT Me-109G/6
Germany
Wing span 9.92m (32ft 6 ins)
length 8.85m (28ft 10 ins)
weight 3,400 kgs (7,500 lb)

MITSUBISHI A6M5 ZERO
Japan
Wing span 11m (36ft 1 in)
length 9m (29ft 6 ins)
weight 2,743 kgs (6,047 lb)

DEWOITINE D. 520
France
Wing span 10.2m (33ft)
length 8.6m (28ft 3 ins)
weight 2,740 kgs (6,040 lb)

REPUBLIC P.47D THUNDERBOLT
United States
Wing span 12.4m (40ft 8 ins)
length 11m (36ft 1 in)
weight 7,675 kgs (16,920 lb)

MACCHI MC-202 FOLGORE
Italy
Wing span 10.58m (34ft 6 ins)
length 8.85m (28ft 10 ins)
weight 2,937 kgs (6,475 lb)

YAKOVLEV YAK-3
USSR
Wing span 9.44m (31ft)
length 8.8m (28ft 10 ins)
weight 2,660 kgs (5,864 lb)

FOKKER D-XXI
Holland
Wing span 11m (36ft lin)
length 8m (26ft 3 ins)
weight 2,050 kgs (4,520 lb)

SUPERMARINE SPITFIRE MK. V
Britain
Wing span 11.23m (36ft 9 ins)
length 9.12m (30ft)
weight 3,065 kgs (6,760 lb)

FAMOUS BOMBERS OF WORLD WAR II

HEINKEL He111
Germany
The most widely used German bomber.

MITSUBISHI G4M
Japan
This was also a highly efficient torpedo-bomber.

LeO-45
France
The most modern bomber used by the French forces.

BOEING B-17
United States of America
Called the "Flying Fortress" because of its formidable array of armament.

CRDA Cant. Z 1007 bis Alcione
Italy
A 3-engined aircraft of great speed and range.

ILYUSHIN Il-4
USSR
Also armed with a torpedo; highly effective.

PZL-37 LOS
Poland
A modern, twin-engined, fast bomber.

SHORT STIRLING
Britain
A well-armed, four-engined heavy bomber.

AIR FORCE MARKINGS

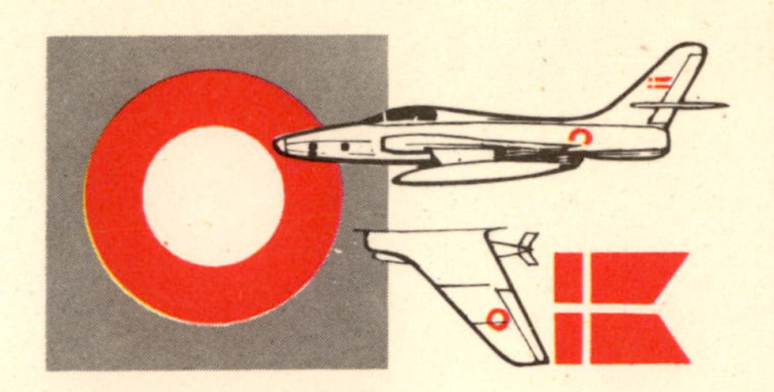

Denmark - Flyvevapnet

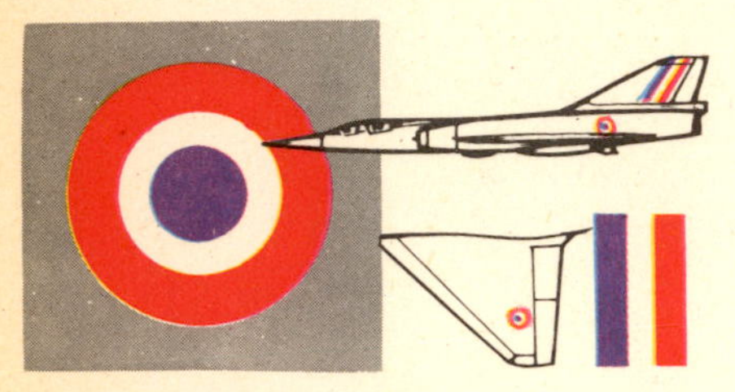

France - Armée de l'Air

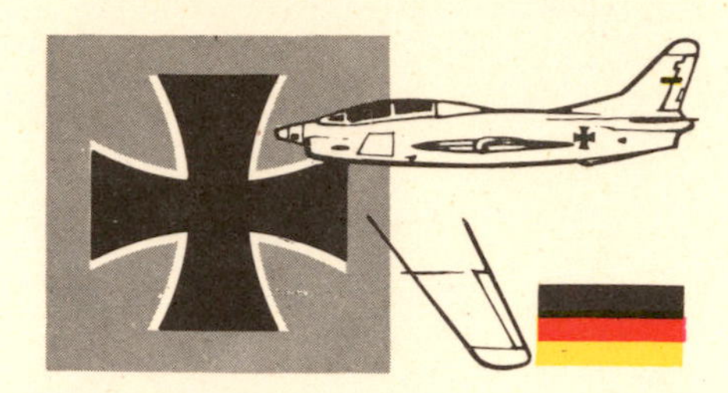

West Germany - Luftwaffe

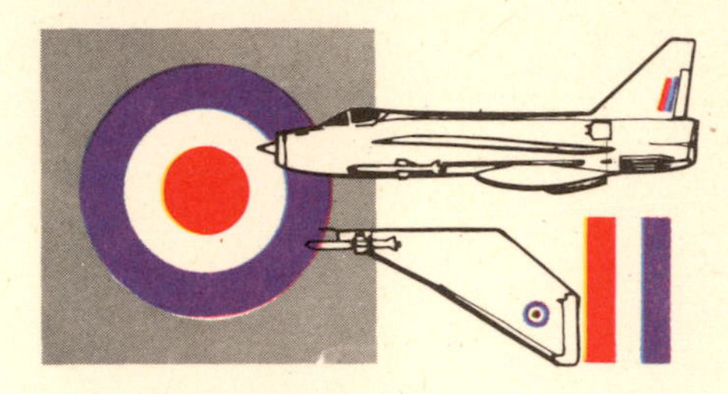

Britain - Royal Air Force

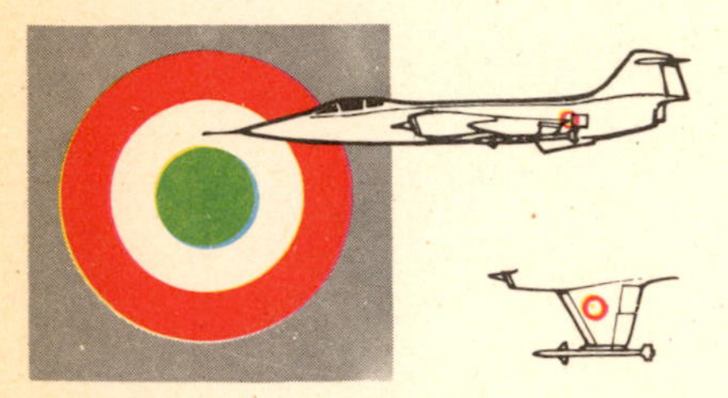

Italy - Aeronautica Militare

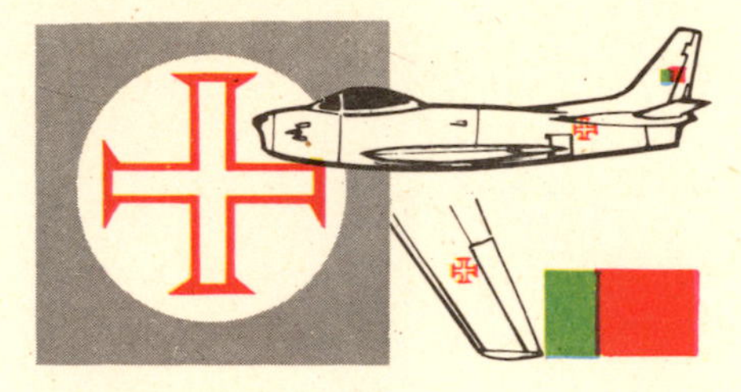

Portugal - Força Aérea

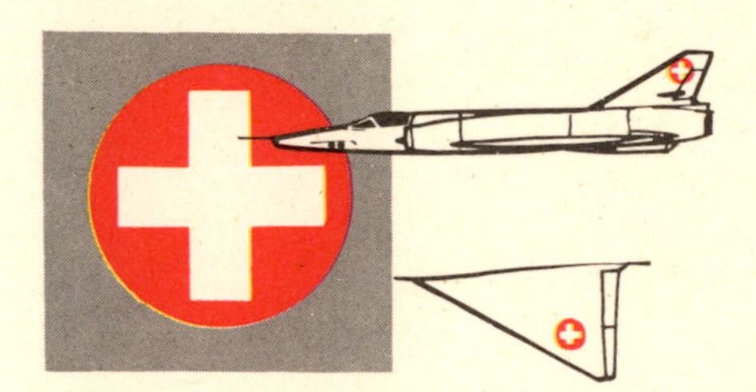

Switzerland - Flugwaffe

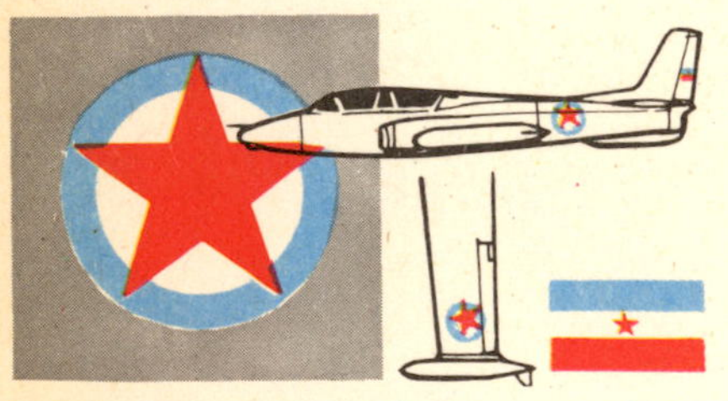

Jugoslavia - Ratno Vazduhoplovstvo

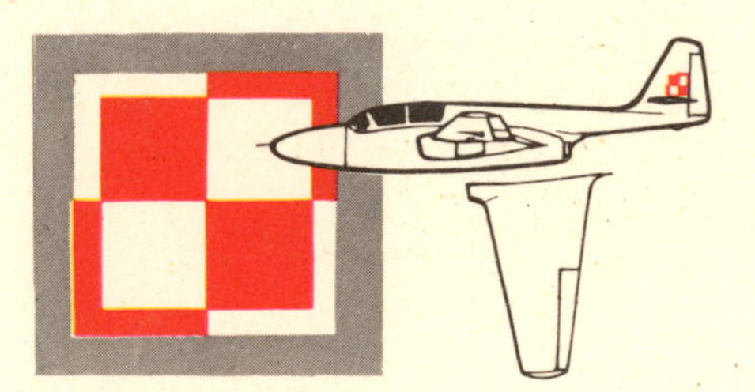

Poland - Lotnictwo Wojskowe

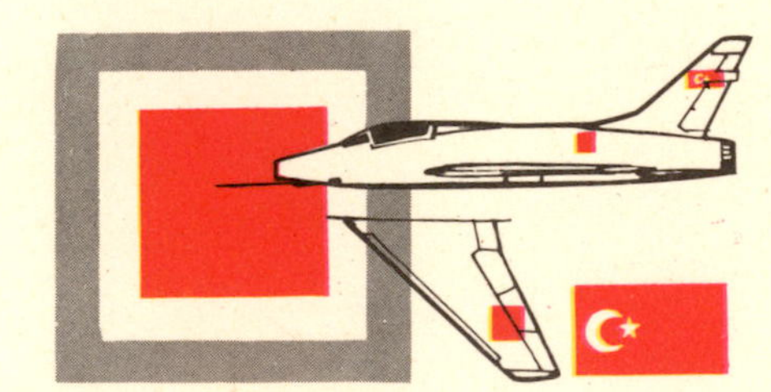

Turkey - Hava Kuvvetleri

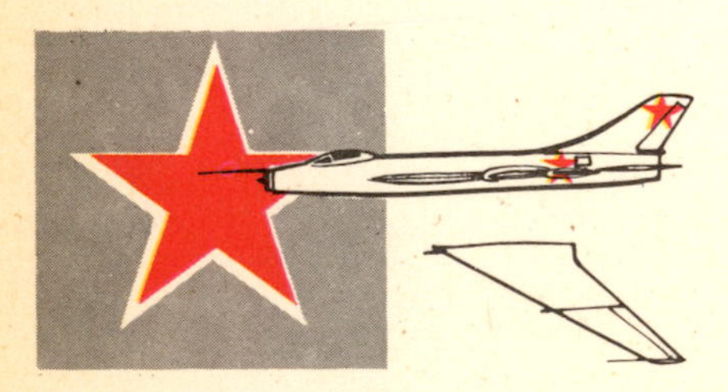

Soviet Union - Voenne Vozdushnyi Sili

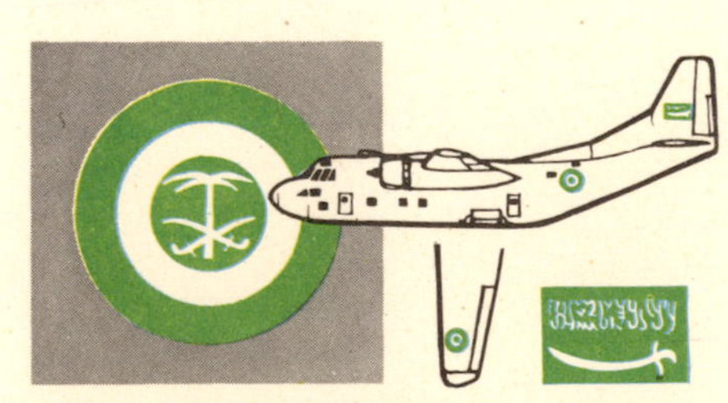

Saudi Arabia - Selah Altayaran Almalaky El Arabi As Saudi

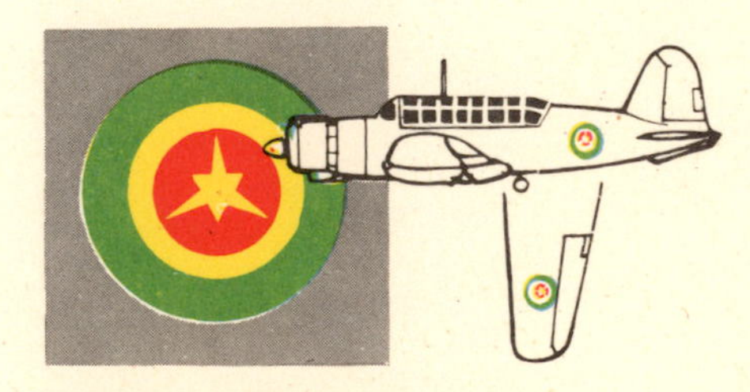

Ethiopia - Ye-Ityopia Ayer Hayl

Iraq - Al Selah Algiaui Al Iraki

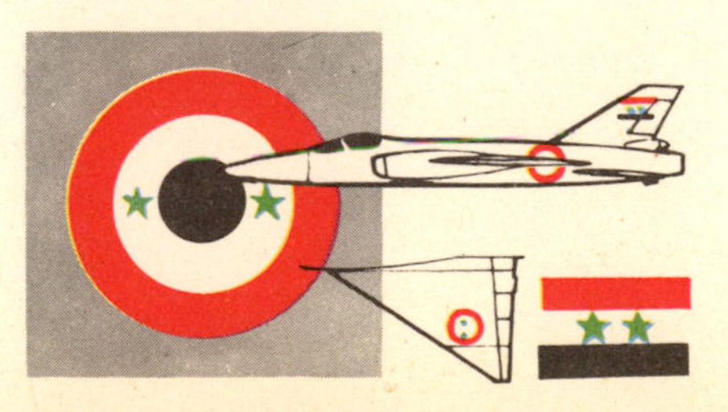

Egypt - UAR - El Couat EL Gauia

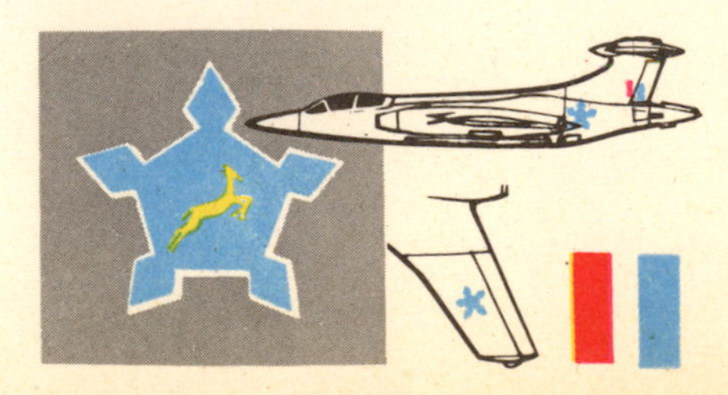

South Africa - Suid Afrik

AIR FORCE MARKINGS

Canada - Canadian Armed Forces

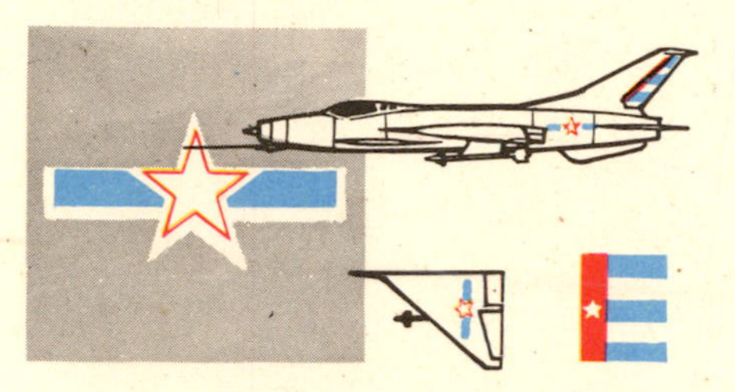

Cuba - Fuerza Aérea Revolucionaria

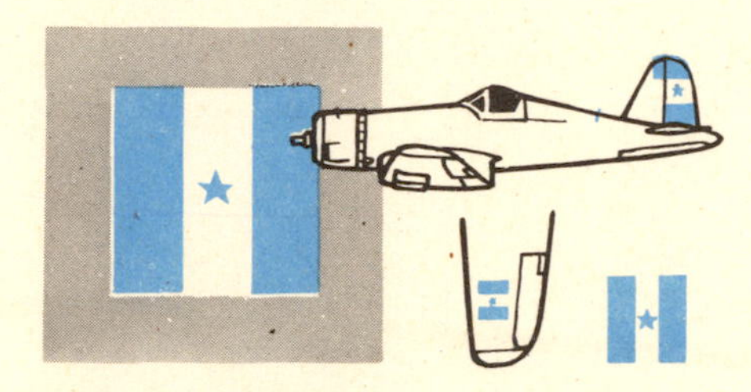

Honduras - Fuerza Aérea

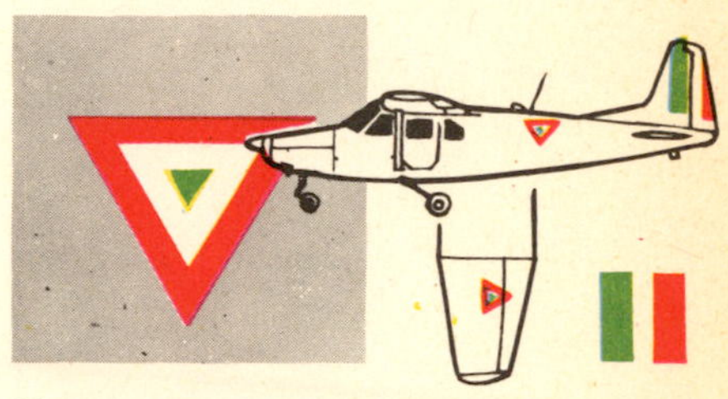

Mexico - Fuerza Aérea

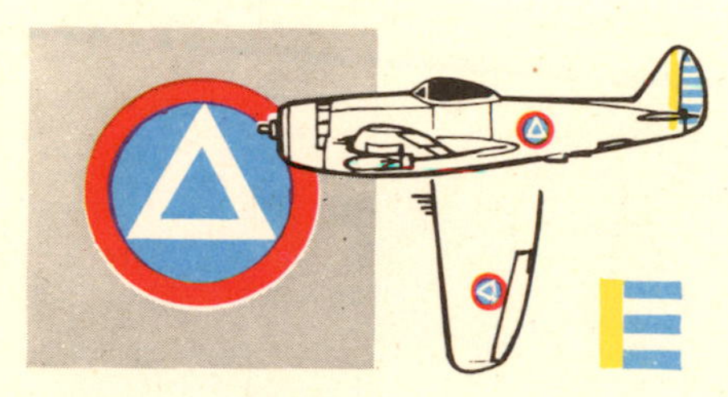

Nicaragua - Fuerza Aérea

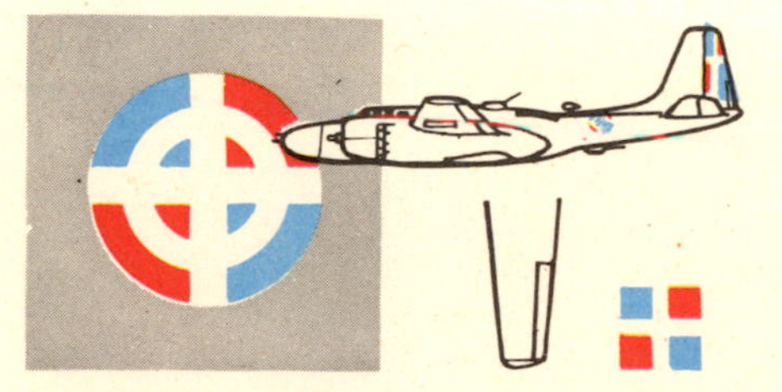

Dominican Republic - Cuerpo de Aviación Militar

USA - US Air Force

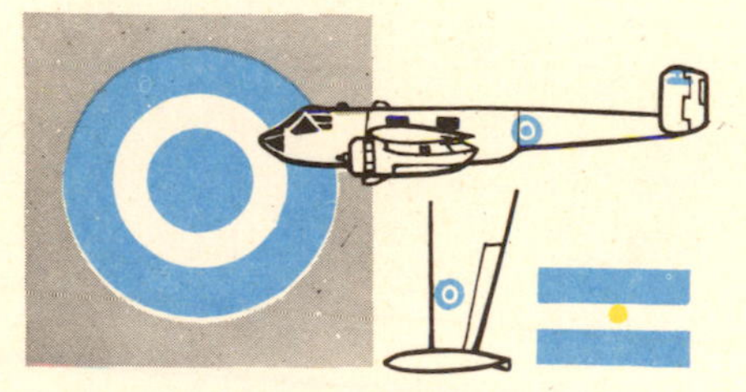

Argentina - Fuerza Aérea

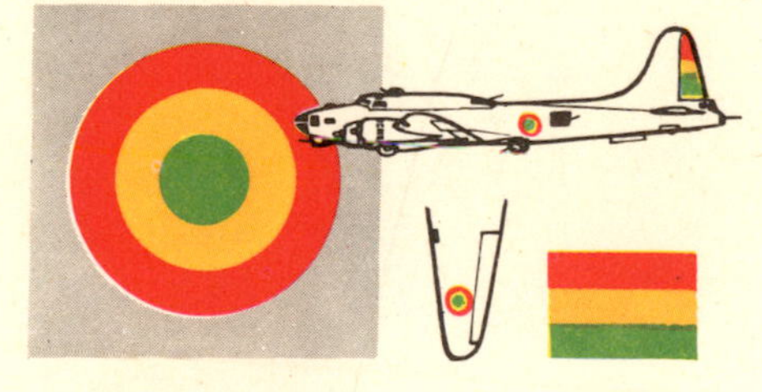

Bolivia - Fuerza Aérea

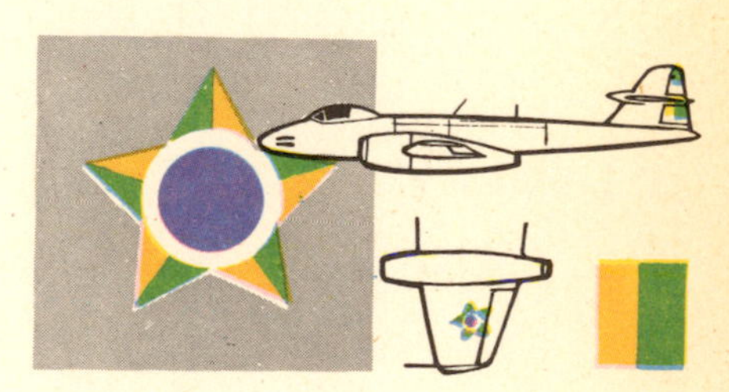

Brazil - Força Aérea

Chile - Fuerza Aérea

Colombia - Fuerza Aérea

Ecuador - Fuerza Aérea

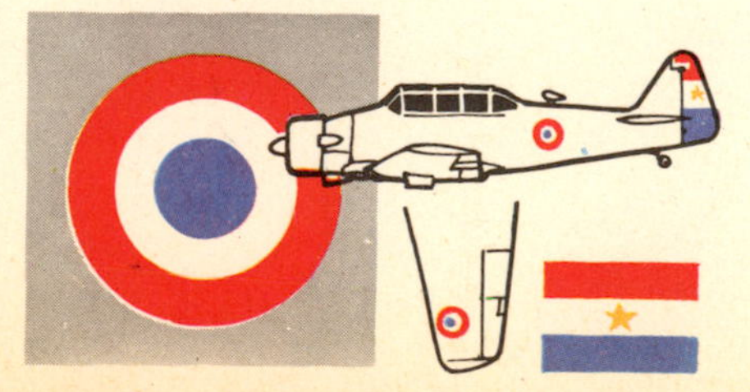

Paraguay - Fuerza Aérea

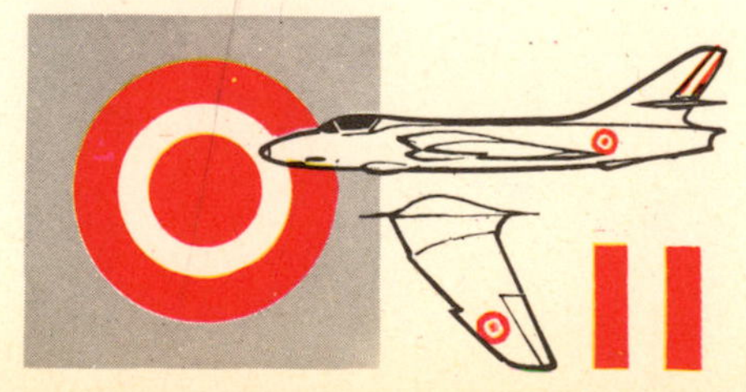

Peru - Fuerza Aérea

Venezuela - Fuerza Aérea

AIR FORCE MARKINGS

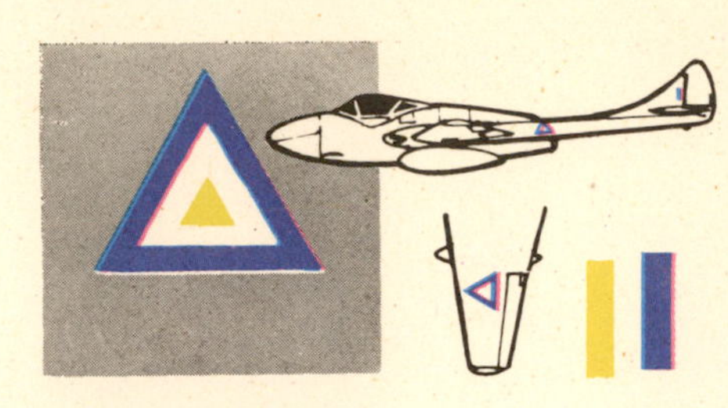

Burma - Tamdaw Lay

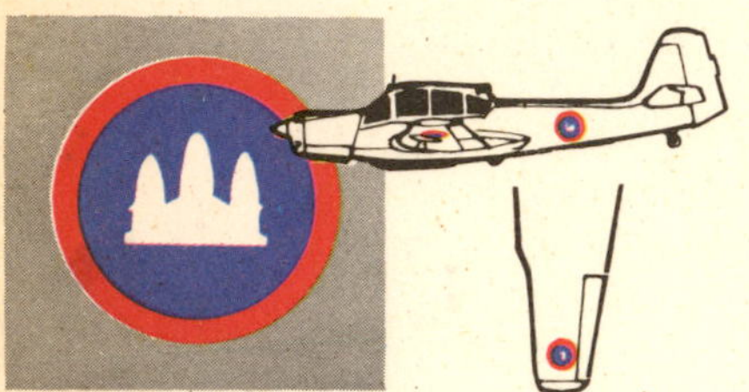

Cambodia - Hank Kmer Khong

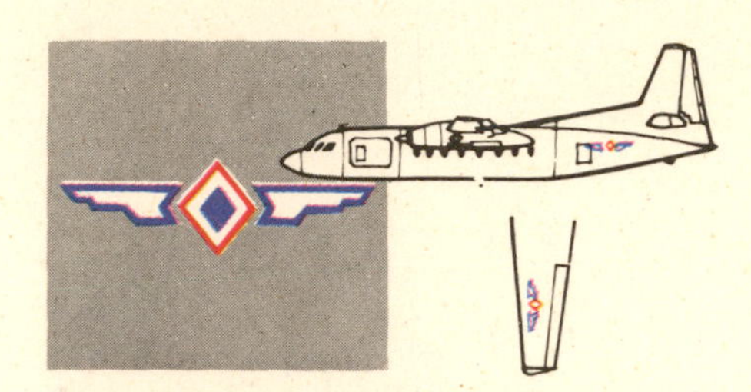

Philippines - Fuerza Aérea de Filipinas

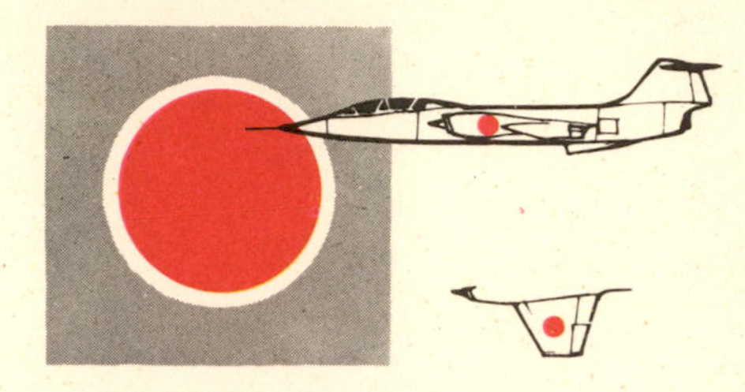

Japan - Koku Jeitai

India - Bharatiya Vayu Sena

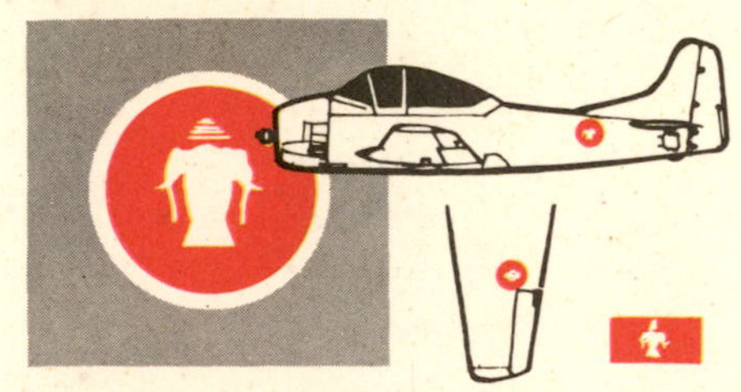

Laos - Service Aérien de l'Armée Laotienne

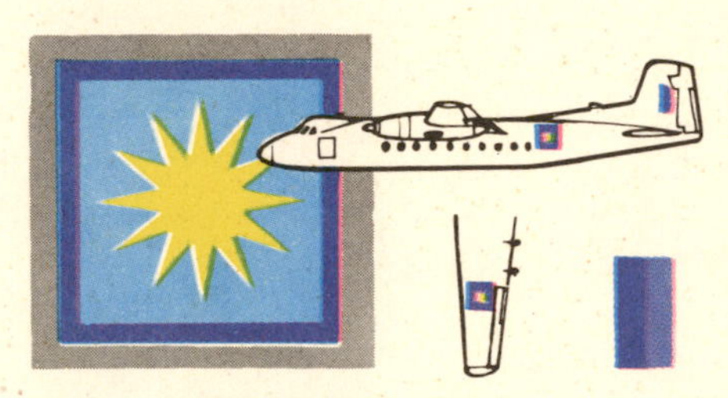

Malaysia - Tentera Udara Diraja Malaysia

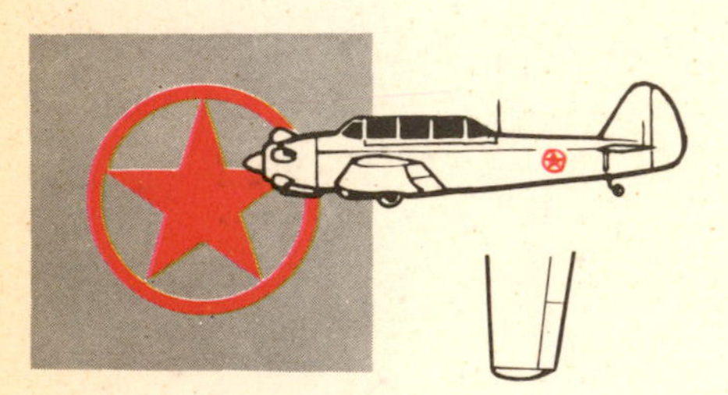

Mongolia - People's Air Force of Mongolia

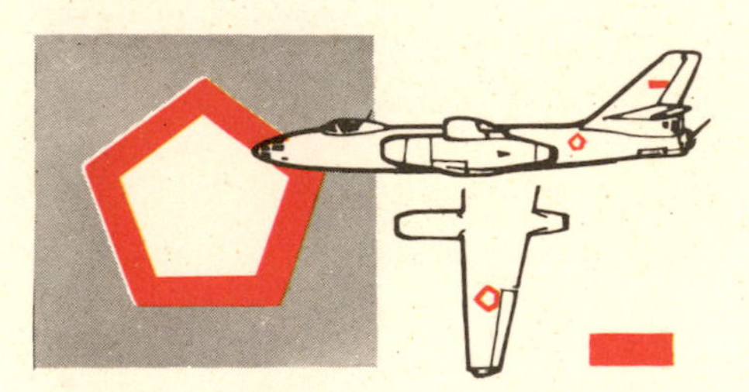

Indonesia - Angkatan Udara Republik Indonesia

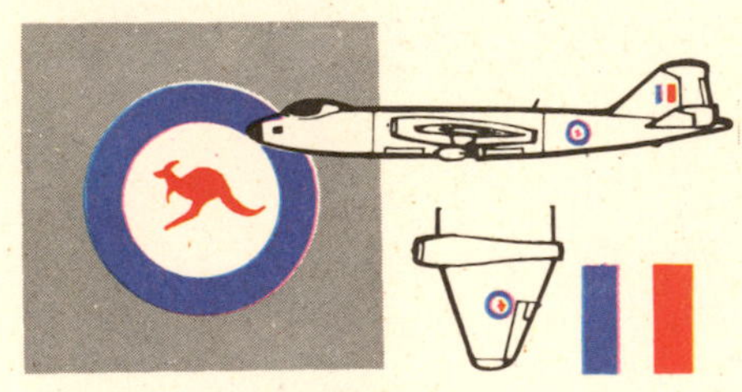

Australia - Royal Australian Air Force

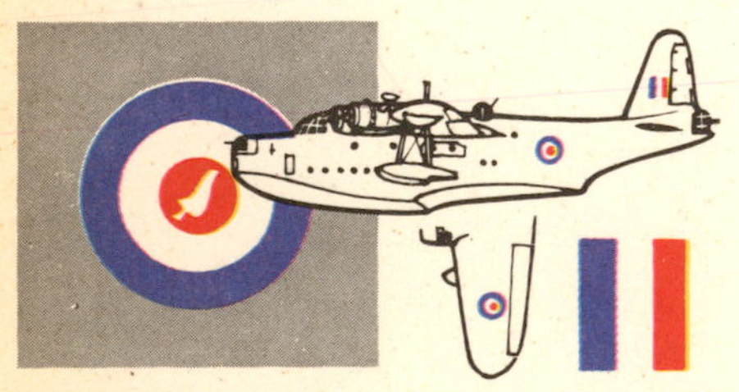

New Zealand - Royal New Zealand Air Force

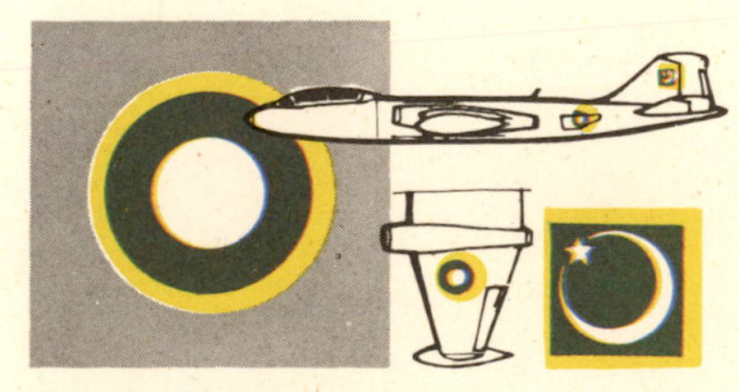

Pakistan - Fiza'ya

Sri Lanka - Rajakiya Lanka Guvan Hamudawa

Republic of China - Min Haiduy

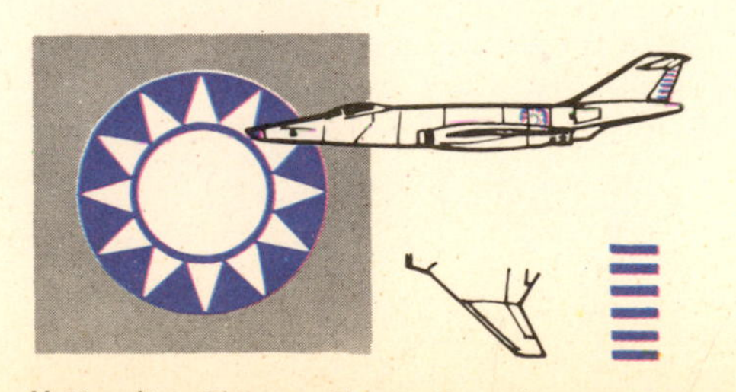

Nationalist China - Chung Hua Min Kuò Kung Chun

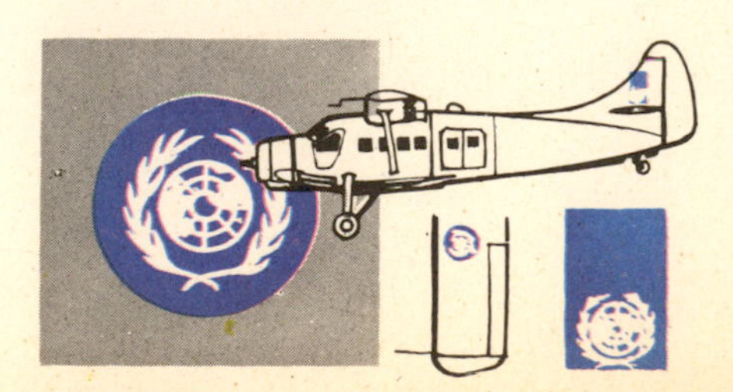

United Nations

The war in Korea

Towards the end of the second World War a new kind of aeroplane appeared which was to outclass all other aircraft — the jet aeroplane. The jet engine is based on Newton's third law — that to every action there is always an opposite and equal reaction. Air is drawn in and compressed, and mixed with fuel. The resultant hot gases escape from the back of the engine, and there is a resulting forward thrust reaction, which drives the aeroplane forward. This new type of aircraft could break through the sound barrier, going well over 700 m.p.h. The jet aeroplane was widely used for the first time in military operations in the 1950 war in Korea. In the same war extensive use was also made of helicopters. Their ability to take off vertically makes them very useful in air rescue operations. They are sometimes more vulnerable to attack than other military aircraft, being incapable of very high speeds, and comparatively slow in take-off and landing. Helicopters currently in use are capable of speeds ranging from about 100 m.p.h. to 200 m.p.h., and faster vertical take-off aircraft are also in service.

The jet aeroplane had first appeared briefly towards the end of the second World War, but the Allies and the Germans did not have time to develop it very thoroughly. By the time war broke out in Korea in 1950, jets were well established, and were widely used in aerial combat. The illustration shows an engagement between American F-86E Sabres and MiG-15s.

1

Civil aviation

1 In the past 25 years jets have gradually taken over from piston-engined aeroplanes, for civil as well as military use. This British-built Trident is one of the fastest commercial aeroplanes in service, reaching a speed of over 600 m.p.h.

2 Powered by four turboprops, this Argosy was specially designed and constructed in Britain as a cargo aircraft. It has large loading doors at both nose and tail. The twin tail makes it very easy to load.

2

3 This VC10 is also British. A large aeroplane, powered by four jet engines, it is used by several commercial airlines. The normal version can carry from 135 to 151 passengers, whilst the "Super" can take from 163 to 180. The four engines are mounted in pairs at the rear.

---

1 When introduced in 1956, this twin-engined Tupolev Tu-104 was one of the first jet aeroplanes to be used in commercial service. Many other types of passenger aircraft were developed from it. The original version carried 70 passengers.

2 The first Boeing 707 was built in 1954. Hundreds of these big four-engined aeroplanes have been built in America, and have proved particularly suitable for intercontinental flights. Many versions were produced. The Boeing 707 carries from 110 to 219 passengers.

3

3 Prior to the development of the huge Jumbo jets, this Russian Tupolev Tu-114 held the record for passenger capacity. It can, in fact, carry 220 passengers. It was first used on the Moscow-Kabarovsk route, in 1961.

4 The big four-engined Lockheed C-141 Starlifter military freighter was built in the USA, and was the forerunner of the huge jet-powered cargo aeroplanes of today. Up to 40,000 kgs (nearly 40 tons) of freight can be carried in its hold.

5 The Ilyushin IL-62, powered by four jet engines, is in service on the major international routes. It is one of the most modern long-range transport aircraft made by Russia, and can fly from Moscow to New York non-stop. It carries 182 passengers.

6 The American DC-9 is a twin-engined jet used by virtually all the big airlines. It is particularly suitable for short and medium-distance flights. The original version carried 90 passengers, but this was later increased. It has a speed of approximately 550 m.p.h.

1

АЭРОФЛОТ
СССР-42383
СССР

2

AMERICAN AIRLINES

3

4

5

Ил-62

6

DOUGLAS DC-9

Civil aviation increased enormously after the second World War, just as it had done after World War I. New air routes were rapidly opened up and civil aviation took on a new importance, as the number of flights increased, and standards of safety improved. Passenger and freight transport and air-mail services came to be accepted as an essential part of everyday life. Gradually people have overcome their doubts about aeroplanes, and now rely on them increasingly, especially for long-distance travel. In terms of the risk of being involved in an accident or being injured, aeroplanes today have a better safety record than motorcars. Unquestionably the most widely used aircraft for passenger transport are jet propelled. Piston-engined aircraft, however, are still used for local passenger and freight transport.

In America in 1933 the forerunners of commercial passenger transport were the Boeing 247 and the Douglas DC-1. Today, 40 years later, Boeing and Douglas are still in the forefront in this section of civil aviation, with their new designs, the Boeing 747 "Jumbo Jet" and the Douglas DC-10. From the point of view of passenger transport, there are two main problems for the civil aviation industry: speed and capacity. The enormous airbuses which are increasingly being used throughout the world, have almost killed the much slower, if more comfortable giant ocean liners. It is expected that in the near future it will be possible to fly from London to New York in less than three hours, by using supersonic airliners to shorten the flight time.

1

1 The French twin-engined Caravelle jet was the first aeroplane to incorporate the revolutionary design feature of rear-mounted jet engines. The Caravelle has a cruising speed of over 500 m.p.h. and carries 80 passengers. It is in service all over the world on short and medium-distance routes.

2

2 Almost 100 airlines have bought versions of this Dutch-built Fokker F-27. First developed in 1955, it is a twin-turboprop aircraft with very low running costs, making for increased profits. It can carry a maximum of 56 passengers.

3

3 This Lockheed Galaxy is a giant among transports. It is 75 metres (248 ft) long, and fully loaded weighs 350,000 kg (about 344 tons). It can carry 100 tons of cargo at 500 m.p.h. over a range of 3,500 miles.

In an attempt to reduce running costs, and in their constant search for an aircraft which is "faster, safer, more comfortable and more modern", the major airlines are currently using real "giants of the air" on their transcontinental routes. Typical of this class of super-airliner is the American Boeing 747, usually called the "Jumbo Jet". Its four jet engines give it a cruising speed of just under 600 m.p.h. It can carry nearly 500 people, passengers and crew, or more than 100 tons of baggage and freight. On board, the passenger accommodation has been made as comfortable as possible, and is divided into different classes. There is a lounge-bar on the upper deck. During the flight, film shows are run, to entertain the passengers, who can listen in to the film in their own language.

Here we see the famous "Jumbo Jet" — the Boeing 747, the luxury liner of the air. It carries up to 490 passengers and is in service on the major intercontinental routes. It is 70 metres (231 ft) long, with a wing span of 60 m (195 ft). It has two passenger decks, as well as a freight deck.

1

Beyond the sound barrier

During the second World War the aviation industry achieved amazing advances, in building new aircraft which were even faster, even more powerful. Traditional piston-engines had been improved and perfected to a point beyond which it was difficult to go. By now, all the famous fighter aircraft of the various countries involved in the war — Spitfires, Messerschmitts, Mustangs — had speeds of around 450 - 500 m.p.h. All attempts, however, to increase speeds still further failed, because of an insuperable technical difficulty. They could, in theory, increase the engine speed as much as they wanted, but beyond a certain engine speed, the efficiency of the propeller was diminished instead of being increased. By now it was clear that if faster aeroplanes were desired, then a completely new approach was needed. A new type of engine had to be invented. At this point aircraft designers started to look into some experiments which had been made some years earlier. These were experiments on turbine engines which could be used in aircraft. The first two working models of this new type of engine had been developed in 1937. On the 12th of April of that year the Englishman Frank Whittle had tested his turbine engine, and in September tests began on aircraft turbines designed by the German Pabst von Ohain of the Heinkel company. The first turbojet-powered aeroplane to fly was German. This was on 27th August 1939, and the pilot was Captain Warsitz. The first British jet plane flew on 15th May 1941. Between these two dates there was the first flight of the Italian-built

2

3

1 The US Air Force for some time used this North American B-70 for experimental purposes. It had six powerful jet engines, and could fly at three times the speed of sound.

2 Skyhawk attack bombers are much used on American aircraft carriers. They are small single-engined jet aeroplanes with delta wings, and can be refuelled in flight. They are very strongly armed, and carry small but powerful missiles.

3 There have been two versions of the American Lockheed A-11, an aeroplane capable of flying at 2,300 m.p.h. at very high altitude: the YF-12A experimental fighter, and the SR-71 which is used for special reconnaissance work. The SR-71 is the fastest aircraft ever to have served with an air force.

1

2

3

Caproni-Campini 1, on 28th August 1940. This aeroplane, however, though it was propelled forward by a stream of gas, did not have a turbine engine, the air being compressed by a piston-engine.

These prototypes ushered in a new era in the history of aviation. Their test flights are as important, historically, as the Wright brothers' memorable achievement, but at the time, in the crisis and confusion of war, few people realised this. Experiments continued, but jets were only "discovered" by the industry at large when it became clear that no further progress could be made with traditional piston-engines.

The turbine engine made it possible to obtain much higher speeds, and it seemed that there was no limit to the speed and size of aircraft which could now be built. So work on the new engines was intensified, and by the end of the second World War the first jet fighters were operational. They did not, however, have the opportunity to demonstrate their real potential, because the war ended only a few months after their entry into service. By now, however, the new direction for aviation was established, and jet-powered military aircraft continued to be built and improved, and became increasingly important. The war in Korea was the testing ground which established beyond doubt the superiority of jets, which could fly at supersonic speeds yet were easily manoeuvrable. Piston-engined aeroplanes were finally abandoned for military use, in favour of turboprops and turbojets, and more and more types and versions of jet-powered aircraft were built.

Naturally, experiments are still going on, even today, to improve the performance of military jet aircraft, but each country is careful not to reveal information about any new development which constitutes a military secret. For this reason, it is only by chance

1 The British Aircraft Corporation's TSR. 2 was designed to give the Royal Air Force a twin-jet attack and reconnaissance aircraft that would fly at more than twice the speed of sound. Although successful, it was considered too costly to build in sufficient numbers for military use.

2 The Swedish single-engined SAAB 35 Draken, with its double-delta wings, and speed of Mach 2, is one of the most highly regarded supersonic aeroplanes made in Europe. It first entered service in 1960, and has a powerful array of weapons.

3 The British-made Lightning also entered service in 1960, and is still one of the most effective fighters of the RAF. The siting of the turbojets, which are mounted one above the other, is both distinctive and highly effective. Various versions of this aeroplane exist, some of which are armed with Red Top missiles.

information leaks, or after some time has passed, that we come to know of the existence of new designs, which have been built and tested under conditions of great secrecy, particularly in Russia.
Among the military aircraft whose capabilities are by now fully known, we can mention the Russian MiG-21 and MiG-25 interceptors, the French Mirage, and the American SR-71A, the last of which can fly at over 2,000 m.p.h. three times the speed of sound.
The American-built experimental X-15 falls into a special category. This was, essentially, a rocket-powered research aircraft rather than an operational jet aeroplane, which was taken up by a huge B-52, before firing its powerful rockets and streaking off on its own across the sky.
In 1961 an X-15 reached a speed of over 4,000 m.p.h. and in 1963 it attained an altitude of 107, 960 metres (67.08 miles). Later, an improved version of the X-15 completed many other test flights, reaching a maximum of 4,534 m.p.h. in 1967. In this way, the X-15 provided information which will be of great value in the further development of supersonic aeroplanes. In particular its test flights, which involved the development and testing of new metal alloys capable of resisting the enormous heat and strain involved at such high speed, will serve as a basis for the construction of future supersonic and hypersonic airliners.
We come, then, to the civil and commercial uses of jet aircraft, now that many years of use have developed them to a level of safety and efficiency no-one could doubt. The first experimental use of a turbine-engined aeroplane on a scheduled passenger flight was in 1950, using a British-built turboprop Viscount. Two years later, in 1952, British

1 Russia has many supersonic military aircraft whose technical quality has, on numerous occasions, been demonstrated. The Tu-22 "Blinder" bomber first entered service in 1961. The turbojet engines are mounted at the rear of the aeroplane. Blinders are armed with missiles.

2 The huge delta-wing Myasishchev bomber known to NATO by the name "Bounder" was the first Russian attempt to produce a supersonic strategic bomber. It did not go into service.

3 Of the many famous Russian MiG fighters, the MiG-21 is one of the most widely used. There are several versions of this delta-winged, supersonic single-engined jet. The early ones were day fighters. Later versions have additional equipment for operation at night or in bad weather conditions.

Comets entered regular airline service, but a series of accidents compelled the manufacturers to withdraw all early Comets from service. Jet aircraft were, in fact, disintegrating in flight. Only after lengthy studies was it discovered that the cause of these disasters was "metal fatigue", which caused the fuselage to buckle, and a subsequent explosion. This defect was eliminated and improved Comets resumed airline service in 1958. In the meantime the Russians had produced their first jet-powered civil aircraft, the Tu-104, a subsonic jet which entered regular passenger service in 1956. The later Tu-114, the largest turboprop passenger aeroplane, can carry 200 passengers non-stop on a flight of over 5,500 miles (Moscow-New York), at a speed of over 450 m.p.h.

The British Comets and the Russian Tupolevs were followed by a succession of other jet-powered civil aircraft from different manufacturers, which gradually took over from the traditional piston-engined aircraft, both on short and long-distance routes.

The largest of this new series of commercial aircraft is the Boeing 747, as has already been mentioned. But, since the introduction of this enormous aeroplane, efforts have been directed towards even more ambitious goals. The first concrete results of these efforts are seen in the Tu-144, which first flew on 31st December 1968, and in the Anglo-French Concorde, whose maiden flight took place a few months later. Both can fly at twice the speed of sound, and have a long range. These aircraft should revolutionise air transport in the next few years, but they pose serious new problems, being noisy.

1

1 The Italian-built FIAT G-91 is a small fighter which was developed to meet a NATO requirement for a tactical aeroplane. It can take off and land in small, rough fields, and carries a considerable array of weapons.

2

2 The French-built Mirage IV is a delta-winged, twin-engined jet. It is a bomber which can, if necessary, carry nuclear bombs, semi-submerged in the undersurface of its fuselage. It can fly long distances by refuelling in flight.

3

3 In the field of supersonic flight, the American X-15 research aircraft has flown faster and higher than any other aeroplane. The X-15 was rocket powered and did not take off in the normal way. To conserve fuel, it was launched from under the wing of a big B-52 at great height.

The age of supersonic flight begins

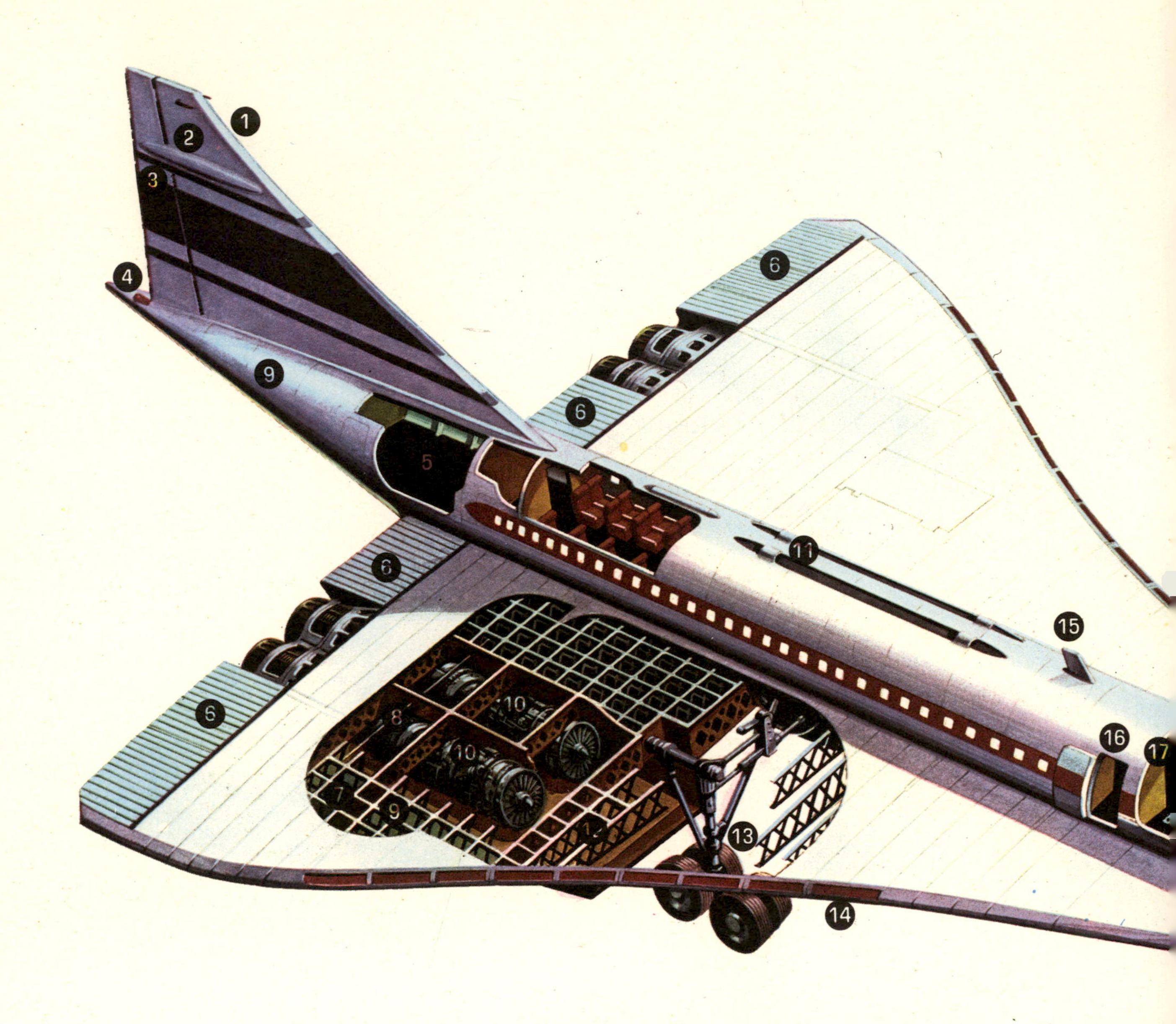

1. Multi-directional antenna
2. Rudder servo control
3. Rudder
4. Fuel jettison
5. Baggage hold
6. Elevons
7. Elevon servo control
8. Afterburner and thrust reverser
9. Fuel tank
10. Turbojets
11. Radio antenna
12. Wing structure
13. Main undercarriage
14. Anti-icing system
15. VHF radio antenna
16. Passenger door
17. Air conditioning system
18. Hand-baggage rack
19. Entrance to hold
20. Forward undercarriage bay
21. Nose undercarriage
22. Service door
23. Navigation instruments
24. Elevon controls
25. First pilot's seat
26. Second pilot's seat
27. Flight controls
28. Droop nose
29. Visor controls
30. Radar
31. Door to galley
32. Nose cone

And so we come to the supersonic passenger aircraft. The Tu-144 and Concorde are a reality. After thousands of hours of test flights, under every type of condition, the two aeroplanes are already available to the airlines, which will use them on major long-distance routes. Their great speed — double that of sound — means that there is the risk that the sonic bang as they travel above the speed of sound might cause damage in built-up areas over which they fly. For this reason they can use their maximum speed only while they are flying over sea or desert, or when flying at high altitude. When passing over inhabited areas, or during the approach to airports, these jets must fly at greatly reduced speeds.

Shown here is a cutaway drawing of the prototype Concorde passenger aeroplane. In this type of aircraft speed is of far more importance than passenger or freight carrying capacity. In terms of capacity there are already in service subsonic jets which are considerably larger; notably the Boeing 747 (490 passengers, maximum take-off weight 351,530 kgs), or the huge American Galaxy freighter (it can carry 100,000 kgs of freight up to 3,500 miles non-stop). In order to fly at twice the speed of sound over long distances it is necessary to limit the number of passengers, both to increase the amount of fuel taken on, and also to make the general structure of the aircraft more suitable for high speeds. Concorde's maximum number of passengers is 128, and the Tu-144 takes between 100 and 140. The pre-production Concorde had an unloaded weight of 91,000 kgs. Its maximum load was 12,700 kgs, and its maximum take-off weight 171,000 kgs. This means that its tanks took the equivalent of 70,000 kgs of fuel. Slight modifications have since been made in these specifications. The general structure of the aeroplane has also undergone modifications after initial tests.

One of the main problems the designers had to solve in this supersonic passenger aircraft concerned the composition of the metals used. Not only did they have to be capable of resisting the strain involved when breaking through the sound barrier, but they also had to withstand very high temperatures. In fact, at Mach 2, even in the freezing temperatures at 20,000 metres altitude, the friction of the air heats the outside of the plane to 150 degrees centigrade. In order, therefore, to keep the temperature inside at a steady 20 degrees C, at high speeds, the heating system has to work as a cooling system. Countless tests have now been conducted on this aeroplane, both on the ground and in flight. Concorde is made up of about 40,000 components, and has an electronic computer on board, which can, at any moment during the flight, make thousands of checks. Concorde was officially born on 29th November 1962, the day on which France and Britain signed an agreement to work together to build what was to be the world's first supersonic passenger aircraft. Work on different sections of the aeroplane was begun simultaneously in the two big experimental centres of Filton near Bristol, and Toulouse, but various technical and political problems delayed progress. Concorde's builders, who had expected to be the first to produce a supersonic passenger aircraft, were beaten into second place, though only by a few months, by the Russians. On 31st December 1968 the Tass Agency announced the first test flight of the huge supersonic Tu-144 designed by Alexei Tupolev, the son of a famous father, Andrei Tupolev. Concorde was not ready for test flight until two months later.

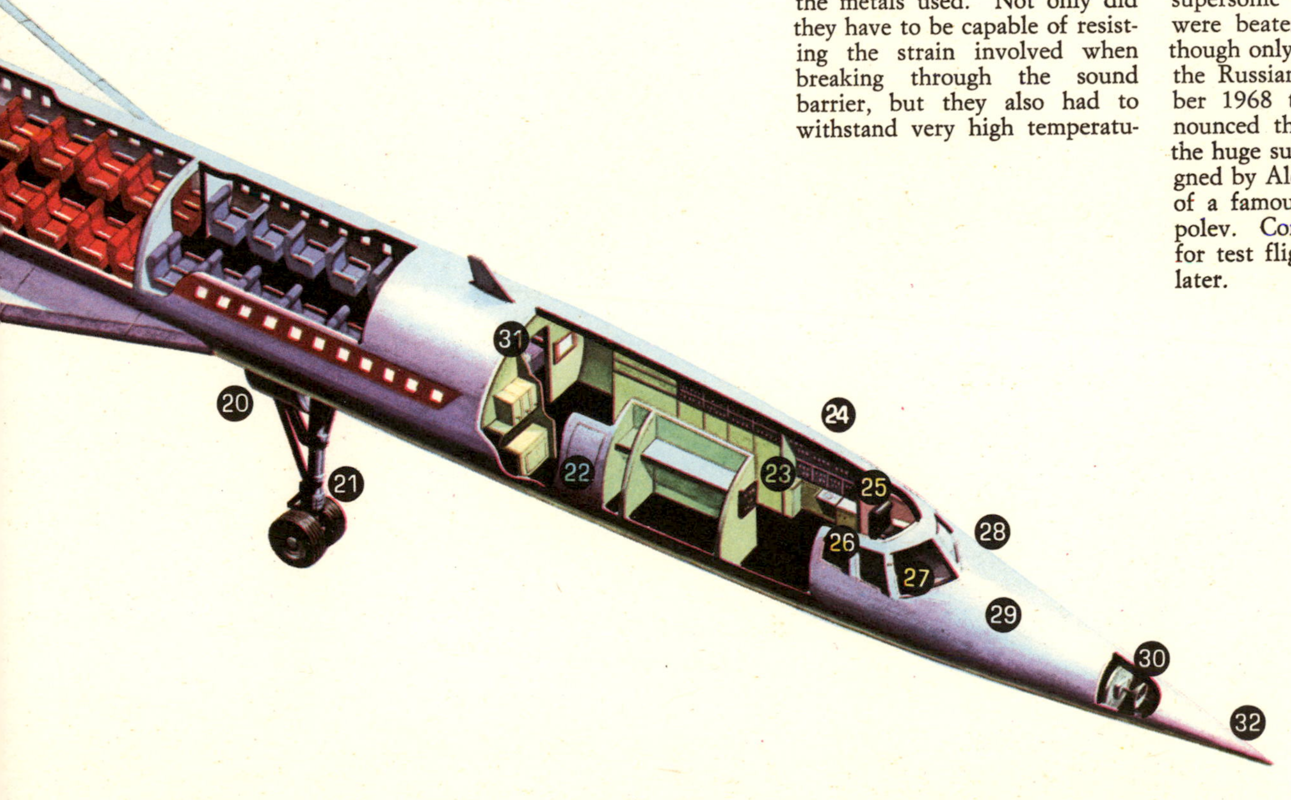

Vertical take-off

1

2

1 This drawing shows an early design for the German Dornier Do 31, a vertical take-off transport aircraft. Clearly visible are the two jet engines, mounted towards the fuselage, for use in horizontal flight, and the two outer groups of small vertically-mounted jet engines, for take-off.

2 One of the many possible ways of solving the problem of vertical take-off which were studied was the one used in the American BELL X-22A. This had four propellers mounted inside cylindrical ducts. Once the aeroplane was off the ground, these moved round through 90 degrees.

3 The design for this Aeritalia G-222 vertical take-off aeroplane is Italian. Intended for both military and civil use, but not built in this form, the G-222 would have achieved vertical take-off by means of vertically-mounted jet engines, installed in the rear of the nacelles for the horizontal turboprop engines.

4 This vertical take-off experimental fighter, the VAK 191B, was the result of collaboration between the Italian and German aviation industries. The main propulsive engine and four vertical lift-jets were all installed in the fuselage.

3

In recent years, while the aviation industry was producing more and more impressive aircraft, both for military and civil use, a few specialists were working along very different lines from the colleagues who had succeeded in building gigantic transports or ultra-fast supersonic aircraft.
The problem they were seeking to solve was one which had concerned aircraft designers for many years: vertical take-off. As aeroplanes had increased in size and speed, it had been necessary to enlarge airports and build progressively stronger and longer runways. With the advent of jet aircraft, with their ultra-high speeds and longer take-off runs, the problem had become even more serious.
By the use of certain technical devices, such as thrust reversers and braking parachutes, aeroplanes had been developed which could take off and land on fairly short runways. Even the problem of jet fighters taking off and landing on the short decks of aircraft carriers had been brilliantly solved. In 1971, at the XXIX Paris International Air Show, two of the biggest transport aircraft in the world were presented, the American Galaxy, 75 metres long, and the Russian Ilyushin Il-76, weighing 150 tons. Both of these were capable of taking off in comparatively short distances, or on grass runways. But not even these achievements satisfied the technicians who wanted, at all costs, to succeed in the ambitious project of vertical take-off. In these pages we show aircraft which have been designed and tested by various manufacturers. Some have been successful, others not. What matters is that, today, vertical take-off aircraft are a reality. Most of the prototypes which were built were purely experimental, and were intended for military development; but V/STOL ("Vertical/Short Take-Off and Landing") aircraft will almost certainly be built in the future for civil use, just as happened with jet aircraft. When this does happen, it will finally solve one of the biggest problems of airports, which even today are inadequate to cope with the ever-increasing volume of air traffic.

1 Another European design for a vertical take-off aeroplane was this special version of the French Mirage fighter, which had one turbojet engine for propulsion, and a further eight for lift. It was known as the Mirage III-V.

2 The British-built Hawker Siddeley P.1127 was the forerunner of the Harrier, the first single-engined vertical take-off jet aeroplane to enter service. The turbojet has four rotating exhaust nozzles, which are turned downwards during take-off and landing.

1

2

AEROBATICS

For the daredevil pioneers of flight, the urge to perform aerobatics with their aircraft must have been an irresistible temptation, once they realised that they could retain control even when the aircraft was in positions very different from the normal flying attitude. It is therefore difficult to establish who was the first aerobatic ace. Illustration 1 depicts a moment from the famous loop performed by Adolphe Pégoud in a Blériot monoplane on

2nd September 1913. One of the greatest exponents of aerobatics was the German Ernst Udet, shown in illustration 2 in his "Flamingo" biplane in 1928. In illustration 3 we see several Fiat CR.32 biplanes of the Italian aerobatic team which was famous during the years between the two world wars for its amazing exploits.
The advent of high-speed jet aircraft has made formation aerobatics even more interesting and competitive, especially when performed by fighter aircraft. Even if the aeroplanes have changed, the main aerobatic manoeuvres performed by piston-engined aircraft have remained the same since the time of the pioneers. We show them below:
A. Immelmann Turn. B. Wingover. C. Stall Turn. D. Loop. E. Roll off the Top of a Loop. F. Cuban Eight. G. Horizontal Roll. H. Barrel Roll. I. Vertical Roll.

B

C

E

F

H

I

The Helicopter

1 The Autogiro may be considered the forerunner of the modern helicopter. It was perfected by the Spaniard Juan de La Cierva, who was the first man to apply the principle of rotating wings to an aircraft with entire success. This Autogiro was built in 1928.

2 The American Sikorsky S-64 Skycrane is a very specialized type of helicopter. It is, in effect, a flying crane, capable of lifting and transporting very heavy and bulky loads. It is used where terrain is uneven, or where there are no roads.

The helicopter is much newer than the aeroplane, but has already been of great service to man. Historians usually say that Leonardo da Vinci produced the first design for a helicopter. Others quote names of inventors and builders nearer to our times; but it was in 1946 that, for the first time ever, a helicopter received a certificate of airworthiness. This was the document which opened a new chapter in the history of the helicopter, and ended its pioneering era. And so, today, the helicopter is with us, used everywhere, doing jobs which only this marvellous flying machine could perform. Its major advantage lies in its ability to take off and land in a minimum of space. It also has the advantage of being able to hover in the air, as if hanging from an invisible thread. There is no magic in this: it is due to the fact that the lift developed by its rotor blades balances the weight of the craft.

With a helicopter you can fly almost anywhere, and a skilful pilot can make use of the versatility and manoeuvrability of the craft to do what he likes with it. The first helicopter passenger service was operated in 1950 in Britain, but the commercial use of helicopters has increased only slowly, due to high operating costs. Military use, however, has undergone and enormous expansion, as was demonstrated first in Korea and subsequently in the long drawn-out war in Vietnam, and in other wars which have broken out since 1945.

1

2

3

4

1 **One of the biggest helicopters in the world is the Russian Mi-6, which has set up many world records. It is powered by two large turbine engines, and has a wide opening at the rear to permit the loading of exceptionally large items.**

2 **The British-built Westland Wessex is typical of military helicopters. It was designed and built specially for tactical use, above all for transporting assault troops. Many versions of this helicopter exist.**

3 **Civil uses of the helicopter are not limited to the transporting of freight and passengers. Helicopters have proved very useful in agriculture, especially in the fight against parasites which destroy plants or crops, and in sowing, and in patrolling the countryside.**

4 **There are few limits to the helicopter's usefulness. By now many police forces have them, and on countless occasions they have been proved indispensable in life-saving operations.**

AIRLINE INSIGNIA

British Airways - Britain

Aeroflot - USSR

Air France - France

Iberia - Spain

Polskie Linie Lotnicze - Poland

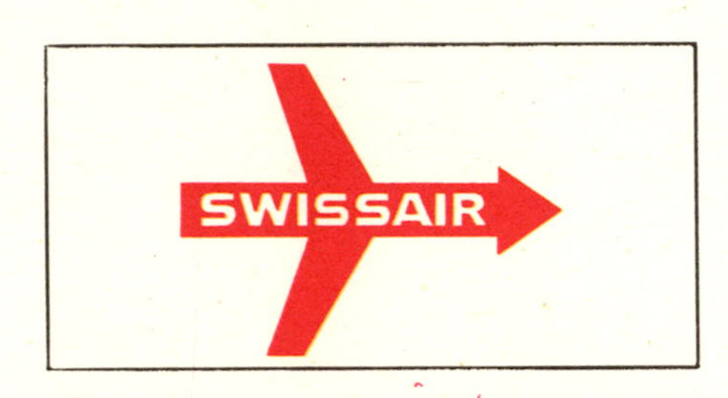

Swissair - Switzerland

Japan Air Lines - Japan

Alitalia - Italy

Middle East/Airliban - Lebanon

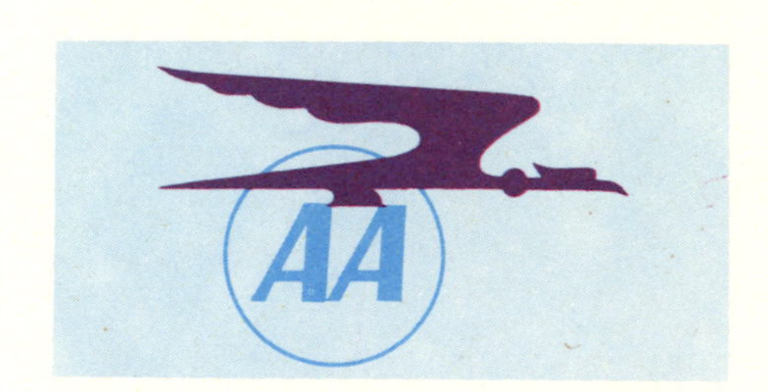

Aerolineas Argentinas - Argentina

Pan American World Airways - United States of America

KLM - Holland

Scandinavian Airlines System - Scandinavia

Trans World Airlines - United States of America

Lufthansa - Germany

Finnair - Finland